D0300084

Edexcel Certificate/International GCSE

Chemistry

This book covers the **Edexcel Level 1/Level 2 Certificate in Chemistry** and the **Edexcel International GCSE in Chemistry**.

It's also great for the Edexcel Certificate/International GCSE in **Science (Double Award)** — but you won't need to learn the Paper 2 material if you're doing this course.

How to get your free Online Edition

This book includes a **free** Online Edition you can read on your computer or tablet wherever you have an internet connection.

To get it, just go to **cgpbooks.co.uk/extras** and enter this code...

0550 5434 4819 4723

This code only works for one person. If somebody else has used this book before you, they might have already claimed the Online Edition.

Complete Revision and Practice

Contents

Contents

Edexcel Certificate Exam Information

1) You have to do two exams for the Edexcel Certificate in Chemistry — Paper 1 and Paper 2.

2) Paper 1 is <u>2 hours</u> long and worth <u>120 marks</u>.   *If you're doing the International GCSE in Chemistry, it works*

3) Paper 2 is just <u>1 hour</u> long, and it's worth <u>60 marks</u>. *in exactly the same way — so you'll do two papers too.*

4) Some material in the specification will only be tested in Paper 2. The Paper 2 material in this book is marked with a <u>burgundy 'Paper 2' border</u>. The 'Warm-Up Questions' that cover Paper 2 material are <u>printed in burgundy</u> and the 'Exam Questions' are marked with this <u>stamp</u>: | PAPER 2 |

Remember, if you're doing the Edexcel Certificate/International GCSE in Science (Double Award) you don't need to learn the Paper 2 material.

Published by CGP

From original material by Paddy Gannon.

Editors:
Katherine Faudemer, Rachel Kordan, David Maliphant, Rachael Marshall, Sarah Pattison,
Camilla Simson, Hayley Thompson.

Contributors:
Mike Dagless, Mike Thompson.

ISBN: 978 1 78294 183 5

With thanks to Glenn Rogers and Sophie Scott for the proofreading.
With thanks to Laura Jakubowski for the copyright research.

With thanks to iStockphoto for permission to reproduce the photo on page 72.

Graph to show trend in atmospheric CO_2 concentration and global temperature on page 75 based on
data by EPICA Community Members 2004 and Siegenthaler et al 2005.

Printed by Elanders Ltd, Newcastle upon Tyne.
Clipart from Corel®

Based on the Classic CGP style created by Richard Parsons.

Text, design, layout and original illustrations © Coordination Group Publications Ltd. (CGP) 2014
All rights reserved.

Photocopying more than one chapter of this book is not permitted. Extra copies are available from CGP.
0870 750 1242 • www.cgpbooks.co.uk

States of Matter

You can explain quite a bit of the stuff in Chemistry if you can get your head round this lot.

The Three States of Matter — Solid, Liquid and Gas

Materials come in three different forms — solid, liquid and gas. These are the Three States of Matter. Which state you get (solid, liquid or gas) depends on how strong the forces of attraction are between the particles of the material. How strong the forces are depends on THREE THINGS:

a) the material   b) the temperature   c) the pressure.

Solids

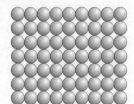

1) In solids, there are strong forces of attraction between particles, which holds them close together in fixed positions to form a very regular lattice arrangement.

2) The particles don't move from their positions, so all solids keep a definite shape and volume, and don't flow like liquids.

3) The particles vibrate about their positions — the hotter the solid becomes, the more they vibrate (causing solids to expand slightly when heated).

Liquids

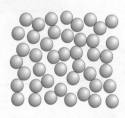

1) In liquids, there is a weak force of attraction between the particles. They're randomly arranged and free to move past each other, but they tend to stick closely together.

2) Liquids have a definite volume but don't keep a definite shape, and will flow to fill the bottom of a container.

3) The particles are constantly moving with random motion. The hotter the liquid gets, the faster they move. This causes liquids to expand slightly when heated.

Gases

1) In gases, the force of attraction between the particles is very weak — they're free to move and are far apart. The particles in gases travel in straight lines.

2) Gases don't keep a definite shape or volume and will always fill any container.

3) The particles move constantly with random motion. The hotter the gas gets, the faster they move. Gases either expand when heated, or their pressure increases.

States of Matter

Materials don't just stay in one state. They can <u>change</u> between all three. Clever eh. It all depends on how much <u>energy</u> they have. Read on...

Substances Can **Change** from **One State to Another**

<u>Physical changes</u> don't change the particles — just their <u>arrangement</u> or their <u>energy</u>.

3) At a <u>certain temperature</u>, the particles have enough energy to <u>break free</u> from their positions. This is called <u>MELTING</u> and the <u>solid</u> turns into a <u>liquid</u>.

4) When a liquid is <u>heated</u>, again the particles get even <u>more</u> energy.

2) This makes the particles vibrate <u>more</u>, which <u>weakens</u> the <u>forces</u> that hold the solid together. This makes the solid <u>expand</u>.

5) This energy makes the particles move <u>faster</u>, which <u>weakens</u> and <u>breaks</u> the bonds holding the liquid together.

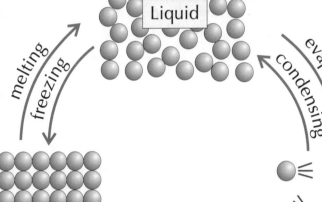

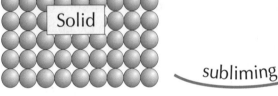

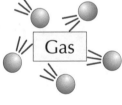

melting / freezing

evaporating / condensing

subliming

1) When a solid is <u>heated</u>, its particles gain more <u>energy</u>.

6) At a <u>certain temperature</u>, the particles have <u>enough</u> energy to <u>break</u> their bonds. This is called <u>EVAPORATING</u> and the <u>liquid</u> turns into a <u>gas</u>.

A red arrow means heat is supplied

A blue arrow means heat is given out

Phew, what a page — particle-ularly gripping stuff...

I think it's pretty clever the way you can explain all the differences between solids, liquids and gases with just a page of pink snooker balls. Anyway, that's the easy bit. The not-so-easy bit is learning it all.

Movement of Particles

There are many nifty experiments that you can do to observe the wonders of chemistry. Here are a few...

Diffusion is the Movement of Particles Through a Liquid or Gas

Diffusion is the gradual movement of particles from places where there are lots of them
to places where there are fewer of them. It's just the natural tendency for stuff to spread out.
You can use the experiment below to demonstrate diffusion...

Potassium Manganate(VII) and Water

Potassium manganate(VII) is great for this experiment because it's bright purple.

1) If you take a beaker of water and place some potassium manganate(VII) at the bottom,
    the purple colour slowly spreads out to fill the beaker.

2) This is chemistry in action (groan)... The particles of potassium manganate(VII) are diffusing out
    among the particles of water.

3) It's the random motion of particles in a liquid (see page 1) that causes the purple colour to
    eventually be evenly spread out throughout the water.

*Potassium Manganate(VII) solution can be **diluted** by adding water*

If you were to add more water
to the final purple solution,
the potassium manganate(VII)
particles would spread even
further apart and the solution
would be less purple. This is
called dilution.

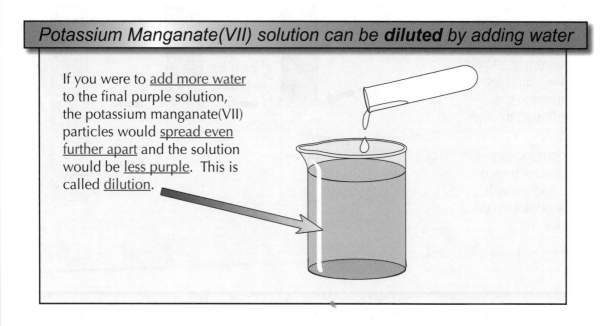

Movement of Particles

Here are two more experiments that demonstrate diffusion...

Ammonia and Hydrogen Chloride

1) Aqueous ammonia (NH_3) gives off ammonia gas.
   Hydrochloric acid (HCl) gives off hydrogen chloride gas.
2) If you set up an experiment like this...

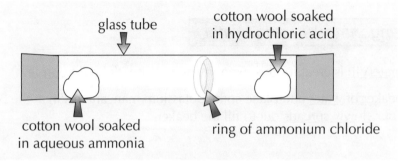

glass tube

cotton wool soaked in hydrochloric acid

cotton wool soaked in aqueous ammonia

ring of ammonium chloride

...you'll get a white ring of ammonium chloride forming in the glass tube.

3) The NH_3 gas diffuses from one end of the tube and the HCl gas diffuses from the other. When they meet they react to form ammonium chloride.
4) The ring doesn't form exactly in the middle of the glass tube — it forms nearest the end of the tube where the hydrochloric acid was.
5) This is because the particles of ammonia are smaller and lighter than the particles of hydrogen chloride, so they diffuse through the air more quickly.

Bromine Gas and Air

1) Bromine gas is a brown, strongly smelling gas. You can use it to demonstrate diffusion in gases.
2) Fill half a gas jar full of bromine gas, and the other half full of air — separate the gases with a glass plate.
3) When you remove the glass plate, you'll see the brown bromine gas slowly diffusing through the air.
4) The random motion of the particles means that the bromine will eventually diffuse right through the air.

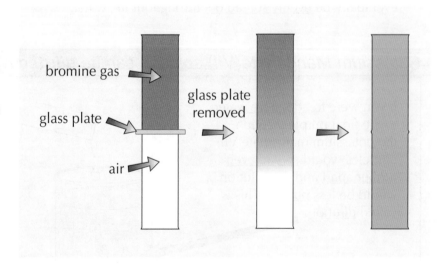

bromine gas

glass plate

air

glass plate removed

Sleeping on the book won't make the words diffuse into your head...

If you're lucky, you might get to see these experiments in the lab. Or, your teacher might show you some equally exciting but different experiments to demonstrate diffusion of particles.

Atoms

All substances are made up of <u>atoms</u>. There are quite a few <u>different models</u> of the atom — but chemists tend to like this <u>nuclear model</u> best.

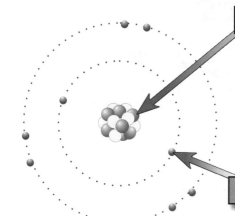

The Nucleus

There's more on electron shells on pages 17-18.

1) It's in the <u>middle</u> of the atom.
2) It contains <u>protons</u> and <u>neutrons</u>.
3) It has a <u>positive charge</u> because of the protons.
4) Almost the <u>whole</u> mass of the atom is <u>concentrated</u> in the nucleus.
5) But size-wise it's <u>tiny</u> compared to the rest of the atom.

The Electrons

1) They move <u>around</u> the nucleus in energy levels called shells.
2) They're <u>negatively charged</u>.
3) They're <u>tiny</u>, but they cover <u>a lot of space</u>.
4) The <u>size</u> of their orbits determines how big the atom is.
5) They have virtually <u>no</u> mass.

PARTICLE	RELATIVE MASS	RELATIVE CHARGE
Proton	1	+1
Neutron	1	0
Electron	1/2000	-1

<u>Protons</u> are <u>heavy</u> and <u>positively charged</u>.
<u>Neutrons</u> are <u>heavy</u> and <u>neutral</u>.
<u>Electrons</u> are <u>tiny</u> and <u>negatively charged</u>.

(<u>Electron mass</u> is often taken as <u>zero</u>.)

Number of Electrons **Equals** Number of Protons

1) Neutral atoms have <u>no charge</u> overall.
2) The <u>charge</u> on the electrons is the <u>same</u> size as the charge on the <u>protons</u> — but <u>opposite</u>.
3) This means the <u>number</u> of <u>electrons</u> always equals the <u>number</u> of <u>protons</u> in a <u>neutral atom</u>.
4) If some electrons are <u>added or removed</u>, the atom becomes <u>charged</u> and is then an <u>ion</u>.

Atomic Number and Mass Number Describe an Atom

These two numbers tell you how many of each kind of particle an atom has.

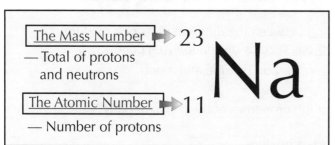

<u>The Mass Number</u> → 23
— Total of protons and neutrons

<u>The Atomic Number</u> → 11
— Number of protons

1) The <u>atomic number</u> tells you how many <u>protons</u> there are.
2) Atoms of the <u>same</u> element all have the <u>same</u> number of <u>protons</u> — so atoms of <u>different</u> elements will have <u>different</u> numbers of <u>protons</u>.
3) To get the number of <u>neutrons</u>, just <u>subtract</u> the <u>atomic number</u> from the <u>mass number</u>.

Molecules are Groups of Atoms

1) Atoms can join together to form <u>molecules</u>.
2) Some molecules are made from just <u>one element</u> (e.g. H_2, N_2), while others are made up of <u>more than one element</u> (e.g. H_2O, CO_2).
3) Molecules are held together by <u>covalent bonds</u> (there's more on bonds on pages 19-20 and 25-27).

Elements, Compounds and Mixtures

There are about <u>100 or so</u> different kinds of atoms and they can join together in <u>loads</u> of <u>combinations</u>...

Elements Consist of One Type of Atom Only

Quite a lot of everyday substances are <u>elements</u>:

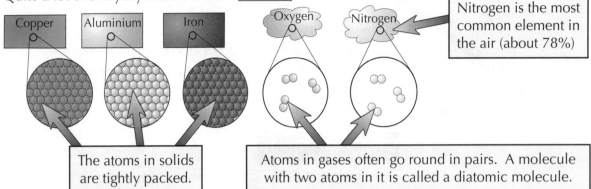

Copper   Aluminium   Iron   Oxygen   Nitrogen

Nitrogen is the most common element in the air (about 78%)

The atoms in solids are tightly packed.

Atoms in gases often go round in pairs. A molecule with two atoms in it is called a diatomic molecule.

Compounds are Chemically Bonded

1) A <u>compound</u> is a substance that is made of <u>two or more different</u> <u>elements</u> which are <u>chemically joined</u> (<u>bonded</u>) together.

2) For example, <u>carbon dioxide</u> is a <u>compound</u> formed from a <u>chemical reaction</u>. One carbon atom reacts with two oxygen atoms to form a <u>molecule</u> of carbon dioxide, with the <u>formula</u> CO_2.

3) It's <u>very difficult</u> to <u>separate</u> the two original elements out again.

Carbon + Oxygen ⟹ Carbon Dioxide

C + OO ⟹ OCO

4) The <u>properties</u> of a compound are often <u>totally different</u> from the properties of the <u>original elements</u>.

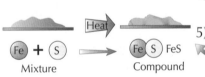

Fe + S ⟶ Fe S FeS

Mixture   Compound

5) For example, if a mixture of iron and sulfur is <u>heated</u>, the iron and sulfur atoms react to form the compound <u>iron sulfide</u> (FeS). Iron sulfide is not much like iron (e.g. it's not attracted to a magnet), nor is it much like sulfur (e.g. it's not yellow in colour).

Mixtures are Easily Separated — Not Like Compounds

1) Unlike in a compound, there's <u>no chemical bond</u> between the different parts of a mixture. The parts can be separated out by <u>physical methods</u> such as distillation (see page 13).

2) <u>Air</u> is a <u>mixture</u> of gases, mainly nitrogen, oxygen, carbon dioxide and argon. The gases can all be <u>separated out</u> fairly easily.

3) The <u>properties</u> of a mixture are just a <u>mixture</u> of the properties of the <u>separate parts</u>.

4) A <u>mixture</u> of <u>iron powder</u> and <u>sulfur powder</u> will show the properties of <u>both iron and sulfur</u>. It will contain grey magnetic bits of iron and bright yellow bits of sulfur.

5) <u>Crude oil</u> is a <u>mixture</u> of different length hydrocarbon molecules — see page 135.

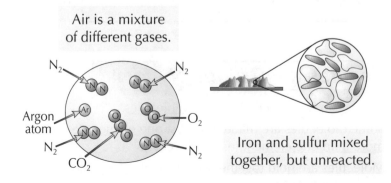

Air is a mixture of different gases.

N_2 N_2 Argon atom O_2 N_2 N_2 CO_2

Iron and sulfur mixed together, but unreacted.

Warm-Up and Exam Questions

Here's a couple of pages of questions to check you've learned all the info.
Have a go at the warm-up questions, then get stuck into some proper exam practice.

Warm-Up Questions

1) Name the two particles that make up the nucleus of an atom.
2) What is the relative mass and charge of each particle in an atom?
3) What is a molecule?

Exam Questions

1 The photograph shows a vessel in a distillery.
The walls of the vessel are solid copper.

a) Copy and complete the sentences about solids
using words from the box. Each word may be
used once, more than once or not at all.

weak	move	colder	hotter	random
strong	expand	heavier	dissolve	regular

In solids, there are .... forces of attraction between particles,

which hold them in fixed positions in a .... arrangement.

The particles don't .... from their positions, so solids keep their shape.

The .... the solid becomes, the more the particles in the solid vibrate.

(4 marks)

b) Inside the vessel, liquid ethanol is turned into ethanol gas.
Describe the changes in arrangement, movement and energy of the particles when
the liquid ethanol is heated to become a gas.

(3 marks)

2 The diagram shows a substance changing between solid,
liquid and gas states.

a) Give the letter of the arrow that
represents subliming.
(1 mark)

b) Give the name of the process
represented by arrow A.
(1 mark)

c) Describe what happens to the particles in a
solid when it is heated to the point of melting.
(4 marks)

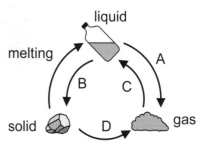

Exam Questions

3   A student placed a small amount of potassium manganate(VII) in a beaker of water.
The potassium manganate(VII) completely dissolved, turning the water nearby purple.
Eventually all the water in the beaker was purple.

   a)   Give the name of the process which made the colour spread through the beaker.

(1 mark)

   b)   The student then added more water to the beaker.
Which sentence correctly explains what happened to the colour of the water?

   A   The colour was unchanged as the amount of
potassium manganate(VII) stayed the same.

   B   The colour was unchanged as water particles
don't react with potassium manganate(VII).

   C   The water got less purple as some of the
potassium manganate(VII) particles reacted.

   D   The water got less purple as the potassium
manganate(VII) particles spread further apart.

(1 mark)

   c)   The result of the student's next experiment is shown below.
A white ring of ammonium chloride has formed on the glass tube
at the point where the hydrogen chloride gas met the ammonia gas.

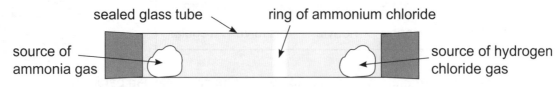

source of
ammonia gas

sealed glass tube   ring of ammonium chloride

source of hydrogen
chloride gas

   Which sentence correctly explains why the ring formed closer to the source of
hydrogen chloride than the source of ammonia?

   A   The air was warmer near the source of the hydrogen chloride,
so it evaporated more quickly.

   B   The particles of ammonia are smaller and lighter, so they diffused more quickly.

   C   The particles of ammonia were diluted by the air in the tube.

   D   The particles of hydrogen chloride gas vibrated about a fixed position.

(1 mark)

4   The photograph shows the NASA Space Shuttle soon after being launched.
The large central tank contains liquid oxygen and liquid hydrogen.
In the shuttle's thrusters, oxygen reacts with hydrogen to produce water vapour.

   a)   Is liquid oxygen an element, compound or mixture?

(1 mark)

   b)   Is water vapour an element, compound or mixture?

(1 mark)

Filtration and Crystallisation

Remember, the components of mixtures are <u>not</u> chemically joined (see page 6).
This means you can <u>separate</u> them <u>very easily</u> using <u>physical methods</u>.

Filtration is Used to Separate an Insoluble Solid from a Liquid

1) Filtration can be used if your <u>product</u> is an <u>insoluble solid</u>
    that needs to be separated from a <u>liquid reaction mixture</u>.

2) It can be used in <u>purification</u> as well. For example, <u>solid impurities</u>
    in the reaction mixture can be separated out using <u>filtration</u>.

Filter paper folded into a
cone shape — the solid is
left in the filter paper.

Crystallisation is Used to Separate
a Soluble Solid from a Solution

Here's how you <u>crystallise</u> a product...

1) Pour the solution into an <u>evaporating dish</u>.

2) Slowly <u>heat</u> the solution. Some of the
    <u>solvent</u> will evaporate and the solution
    will get more <u>concentrated</u>. Stop
    heating when <u>crystals</u> start to form.

evaporating
dish

3) Remove the dish from the heat and leave
    it in a <u>warm place</u> for the rest of the
    solvent to slowly <u>evaporate</u> — this way
    you get nice <u>big crystals</u>.

4) Finally, you've got to <u>dry</u> the product —
    you can use a <u>drying oven</u> or a <u>desiccator</u>
    for this (a desiccator contains chemicals
    that remove water from the surroundings).

Filtration and Crystallisation

Here's how you can put filtration and crystallisation to good use. Separating rock salt...

You Can Use Filtration and Crystallisation to Separate Rock Salt

1) Rock salt is simply a mixture of salt and sand (they spread it on the roads in winter).

2) Salt and sand are both compounds — but salt dissolves in water and sand doesn't. This vital difference in their physical properties gives a great way to separate them.

3) You need to learn the four steps of the method:

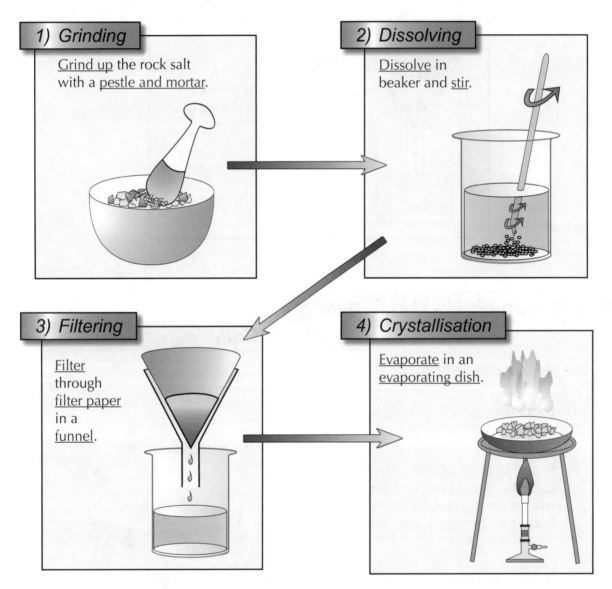

1) Grinding — Grind up the rock salt with a pestle and mortar.

2) Dissolving — Dissolve in beaker and stir.

3) Filtering — Filter through filter paper in a funnel.

4) Crystallisation — Evaporate in an evaporating dish.

4) The sand doesn't dissolve (it's insoluble), so it stays as big grains. These won't fit through the tiny holes in the filter paper — so it collects on the filter paper.

5) The salt is dissolved in solution, so it does go through — and when the water's evaporated, the salt forms as crystals in the evaporating dish.

Revise mixtures — just filter out the important bits...

Before you dash on to the next page (I know, I know, it's just so exciting), make sure you've learnt all the details on this page first. The next page will still be there when you're done.

Chromatography

Chromatography is another method used by chemists to separate out mixtures. You can use paper chromatography to separate out dyes — e.g. in inks, paints, food colourings etc. It's, er, fascinating stuff.

You Need to Know How to Do Paper Chromatography

1) Draw a line near the bottom of a sheet of filter paper. (Use a pencil to do this — pencil marks are insoluble and won't react with the solvent.)

2) Add spots of different dyes to the line at regular intervals.

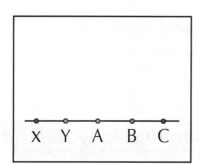

3) Loosely roll the sheet up and put it in a beaker of solvent, e.g. water.

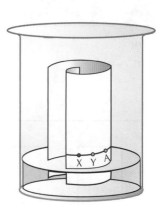

4) The solvent used depends on what's being tested. Some compounds dissolve well in water, but sometimes other solvents, like ethanol, are needed.

5) Make sure the dyes aren't touching the solvent — you don't want them to dissolve into it.

6) Place a lid on top of the container to stop the solvent evaporating.

7) The solvent seeps up the paper, carrying the dyes with it.

8) Each different dye will move up the paper at a different rate and form a spot in a different place.

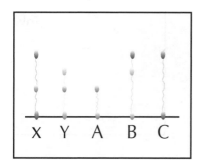

9) The end result is a pattern of spots called a chromatogram.

Chromatography separates dyes in inks

Always draw the line at the bottom of the filter paper in pencil. If you do it in pen, the dyes in the pen's ink will dissolve in the solvent and mess up your results. Which would be annoying.

Chromatography

Now that you know how to do chromatography, it's time to find out how it works.

How **Chromatography** Separates Mixtures

1) Chromatography works because <u>different dyes</u> will move up the paper at <u>different rates</u>.

2) Some will <u>stick</u> to the <u>paper</u> and others will <u>dissolve</u> more readily in the solvent and travel more <u>quickly</u>.

3) The <u>distance</u> the dyes travel up the paper depends on the <u>solvent</u> and the <u>paper</u> you use.

Chromatography Can Help You to **Identify Dyes**

1) If you want to work out what <u>dyes</u> are present in an unknown substance (e.g. an <u>ink</u>), you can use <u>chromatography</u> to find out.

2) First make <u>chromatograms</u> for your unknown substance and for some <u>reference materials</u> (dyes that you think might be in the ink).

3) Now <u>compare</u> the chromatograms to work out <u>what dyes</u> are in your unknown substance — spots on the chromatogram for the unknown substance will <u>match</u> spots on the chromatograms of the reference materials when the dyes are <u>the same</u>.

Example

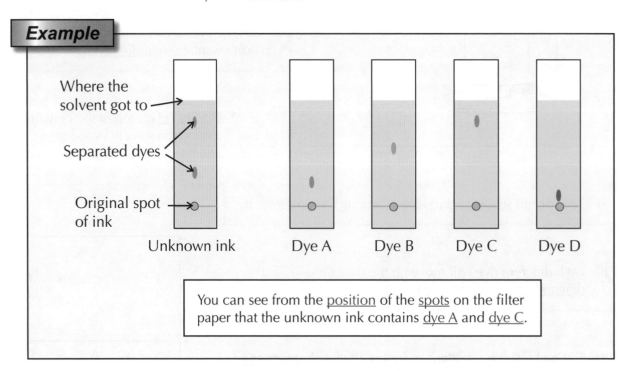

You can see from the <u>position</u> of the <u>spots</u> on the filter paper that the unknown ink contains <u>dye A</u> and <u>dye C</u>.

Different dyes move up the paper at different rates...

So that's chromatography — it's pretty neat once you get your head around it. You can even use it for crime-fighting... CSIs use chromatography to identify unknown substances from crime scenes. They can even use it to identify inks used to print forged money and link 'em back to a suspect.

Distillation

Distillation is used to separate mixtures that contain <u>liquids</u>.
There are two types that you need to know about — <u>simple</u> and <u>fractional</u>.

Simple Distillation *is Used to* Separate Out Solutions

1) <u>Simple distillation</u> is used for separating out a <u>liquid</u> from a <u>solution</u>.

2) The solution is <u>heated</u>. The part of the solution that has the lowest boiling point <u>evaporates</u>.

3) The <u>vapour</u> is then <u>cooled</u>, <u>condenses</u> (turns back into a liquid) and is <u>collected</u>.

4) The rest of the <u>solution</u> is left behind in the flask.

Example

You can use simple distillation to get <u>pure water</u> from <u>seawater</u>.
The <u>water</u> evaporates and is condensed and collected.
Eventually you'll end up with just the <u>salt</u> left in the flask.

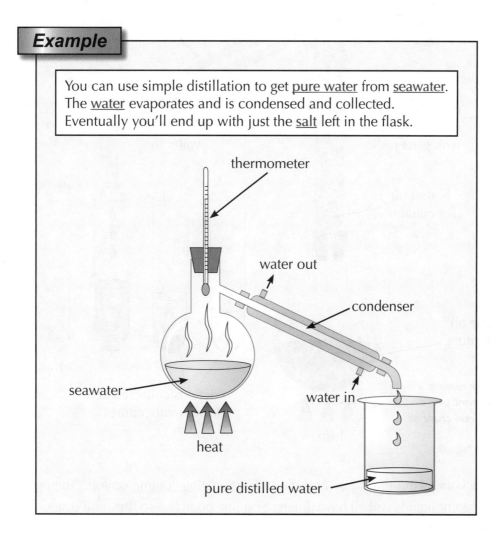

5) The <u>problem</u> with simple distillation is that you can only use it to separate things with <u>very different</u> boiling points.

6) If you have a <u>mixture of liquids</u> with <u>similar boiling points</u>, you need another method to separate them out — like fractional distillation (see next page).

Heating ⟹ Evaporating ⟹ Cooling ⟹ Condensing

You might have used distilled water in Chemistry lessons. Because it's been distilled, there aren't any impurities in it (like ions, see page 19) that might interfere with experimental results. Clever stuff. Make sure you know the ins and outs of simple distillation before you turn over the page.

Distillation

Fractional Distillation is Used to Separate a Mixture of Liquids

If you've got a <u>mixture of liquids</u> you can separate it using <u>fractional distillation</u>. Here is a lab demonstration that can be used to model <u>fractional distillation of crude oil</u> at a <u>refinery</u>.

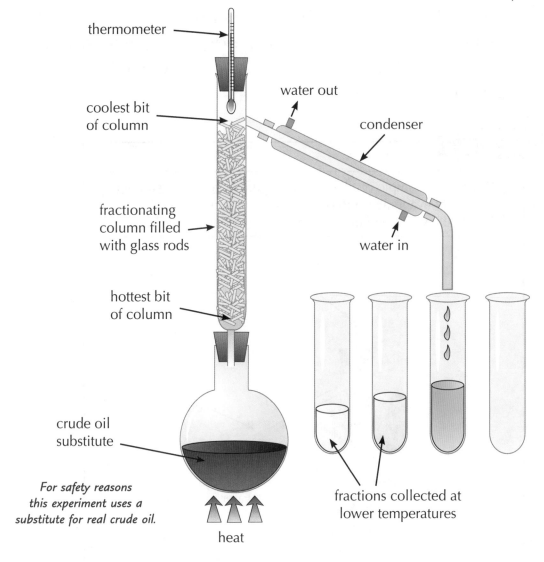

thermometer

coolest bit of column

fractionating column filled with glass rods

hottest bit of column

water out

condenser

water in

crude oil substitute

For safety reasons this experiment uses a substitute for real crude oil.

fractions collected at lower temperatures

heat

1) You put your <u>mixture</u> in a flask and stick a <u>fractionating column</u> on top. Then you heat it.

2) The <u>different liquids</u> will all have <u>different boiling points</u> — so they will evaporate at <u>different temperatures</u>.

3) The liquid with the <u>lowest boiling point</u> evaporates first. When the temperature on the thermometer matches the boiling point of this liquid, it will reach the <u>top</u> of the column.

4) Liquids with <u>higher boiling points</u> might also start to evaporate. But the column is <u>cooler</u> towards the <u>top</u>. So they will only get part of the way up before <u>condensing</u> and running back down towards the flask.

5) When the first liquid has been collected, you <u>raise the temperature</u> until the <u>next one</u> reaches the top.

Fractionating — sounds a bit too much like maths to me...

Remember that parts of <u>mixtures aren't joined together</u> — so you can separate them by <u>physical methods</u>. You need to learn these techniques so make sure you can <u>scribble</u> all this stuff down. Enjoy.

Warm-Up and Exam Questions

Here are some useful questions to check you've learnt all the info.

Warm-Up Questions

1) Which separation technique could you use to separate a soluble solid from a solution?

2) Which technique could you use to separate a mixture of liquids with similar boiling points?

Exam Questions

1   A forensic scientist is using paper chromatography to compare different inks.

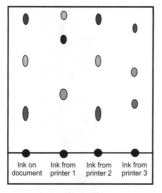

Ink on document   Ink from printer 1   Ink from printer 2   Ink from printer 3

a)   Describe the method used to set up a paper chromatography experiment to compare the inks.

(3 marks)

b)   The scientist is using paper chromatography to compare an ink used on a document with the ink in three different printers. The chromatogram is shown on the right.

Which printers could not have produced the document?

(1 mark)

2   Lawn sand is a mixture of insoluble sharp sand and soluble ammonium sulfate fertiliser.

a)   Describe how you would obtain pure, dry samples of the two components in the lab.

(4 marks)

b)   A student separated 51.4 g of lawn sand into sharp sand and ammonium sulfate. After separation, the total mass of the two products was 52.6 g. Suggest one reason for this error.

(1 mark)

3   The boiling points of three liquids are shown in the table.

Liquid	Boiling point (°C)
Methanoic acid	101
Propanone	56
Water	100

a)   State why simple distillation cannot be used to separate water from a solution of water and methanoic acid.

(1 mark)

b)   The apparatus shown was used to separate a mixture of propanone and water. Copy and complete the table using the options below. Each option may be used once, more than once, or not at all.

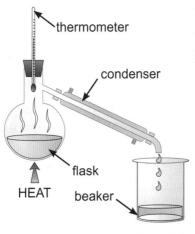
thermometer
condenser
flask
HEAT   beaker

no liquid   water   propanone   both liquids

Temperature on thermometer	Contents of the flask	Contents of the beaker
30 °C		
65 °C		
110 °C		

(3 marks)

c)   Explain how fractional distillation works to separate a mixture of liquids.

(4 marks)

The Periodic Table

In 1869, <u>Dmitri Mendeleev</u> arranged 50 known elements in order of <u>atomic mass</u> to make a Table of Elements. Mendeleev's table placed elements with <u>similar chemical properties</u> in the same vertical <u>groups</u> — but he found that he had to leave <u>gaps</u> in his table to make this work. The gaps in Mendeleev's table of elements were really clever because they <u>predicted</u> the properties of undiscovered elements. Since then <u>new elements</u> have been found which fit into the gaps left in Mendeleev's table...

The **Periodic Table** is a Table of All Known **Elements**

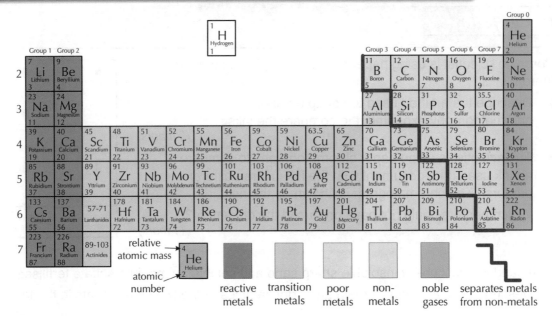

1) We now know there are <u>100ish elements</u> that all materials are made of, with more still being 'discovered'.

2) The <u>modern</u> periodic table shows the elements in order of increasing <u>atomic number</u>.

3) The periodic table is laid out so that elements with <u>similar properties</u> form <u>columns</u>.

4) These <u>vertical columns</u> are called <u>groups</u>.

5) The <u>group</u> to which an element belongs <u>corresponds</u> to the <u>number of electrons</u> it has in its <u>outer shell</u>. (Group 1 elements have 1 outer shell electron, Group 2 elements have 2 outer shell electrons and so on.)

6) Some of the groups have special names. <u>Group 1</u> elements are called <u>alkali metals</u>. <u>Group 7</u> elements are called <u>halogens</u>, and <u>Group 0</u> are called the <u>noble gases</u>.

Elements in a **Group** Have the **Same Number** of **Outer Electrons**

1) The elements in any one <u>group</u> all have the same number of <u>electrons</u> in their <u>outer shell</u>.

2) That's why they have <u>similar properties</u>. And that's why we arrange them in this way.

3) When only a small number of elements were known, the periodic table was made by looking at the <u>properties</u> of the elements and arranging them in groups — the same groups that they are in today.

4) This idea is <u>extremely important</u> to chemistry — so make sure you understand it.

> The properties of the elements depend on the <u>number of electrons</u> they have.
> <u>Atomic number</u> is therefore very significant because it is
> equal to the number of electrons each atom has.
>
> But it's the number of electrons in the <u>outer shell</u> which is the really important thing.

Electron Shells

The fact that electrons occupy "shells" around the nucleus is what causes the whole of chemistry. Remember that, and watch how it applies to each bit of it. It's ace.

Electron Shell Rules:

1) Electrons always occupy shells (sometimes called energy levels).

2) The lowest energy levels are always filled first — these are the ones closest to the nucleus.

3) Only a certain number of electrons are allowed in each shell:

   • 1st shell — 2

   • 2nd shell — 8

   • 3rd shell — 8

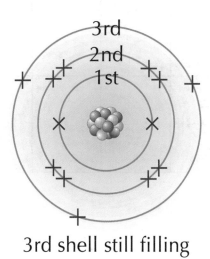

3rd shell still filling

4) Atoms are much happier when they have full electron shells — like the noble gases in Group 0.

5) In most atoms the outer shell is not full and this makes the atom want to react to fill it.

Electron shells — probably the most important thing in chemistry

It's really important to learn the rules for filling electron shells. It's so important I'll leave this page with a quick recap. The energy of the shells increases with increasing number (so shell 1 is the lowest). Fill the shell with lowest energy first. The 1st shell can only hold a maximum of 2 electrons, but the 2nd and 3rd shells can both hold 8 electrons. Practise following these rules on the next page.

Electron Shells

*Follow the Rules to **Work Out** Electronic Configurations*

You need to know the <u>electronic configurations</u> for the first <u>20</u> elements (things get a bit more complicated after that). But they're not hard to work out.
For a quick example, take nitrogen. <u>Follow these steps...</u>

> 1) The periodic table tells us nitrogen has <u>seven</u> protons... so it must have <u>seven</u> electrons.
>
> 2) Follow the '<u>Electron Shell Rules</u>' on the previous page. The <u>first</u> shell can only take 2 electrons and the <u>second</u> shell can take a <u>maximum</u> of 8 electrons.
>
> 3) So the electronic structure for nitrogen <u>must</u> be <u>2, 5</u>. Easy peasy.

Now find the electronic configuration of <u>argon</u> (answer below).

The periodic table has a big gap here where the transition metals fit in on row four.

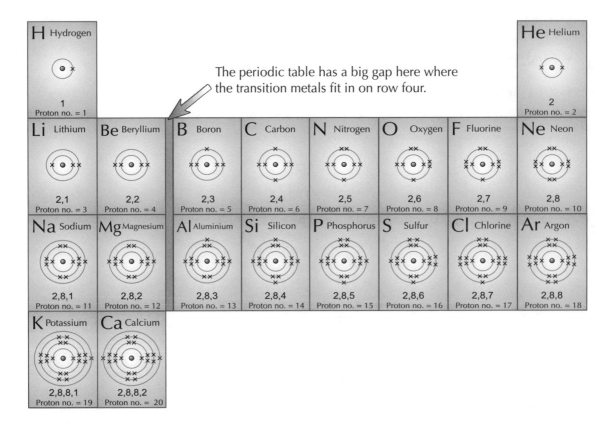

> <u>Answer...</u>
> To calculate the electronic structure of argon, <u>follow the electron shell rules</u>. It's got 18 protons, so it <u>must</u> have 18 electrons. The first shell must have <u>2</u> electrons, the second shell must have <u>8</u>, and so the third shell must have <u>8</u> as well. It's as easy as <u>2, 8, 8</u>.

Each shell can only take a set number of electrons

You need to know enough about electron shells to draw out that <u>whole diagram</u> in the middle of the page without looking at it. Obviously, you don't have to learn each element separately — just <u>learn the rules</u>. Cover the page: using a periodic table, find the atom with the electron structure 2, 8, 6.

Ionic Bonding

Ionic Bonding — ***Transfer*** *of Electrons*

1) In <u>ionic bonding</u>, atoms <u>lose or gain electrons</u> to form <u>charged particles</u> (called <u>ions</u>) which are then <u>strongly attracted</u> to one another (because of the attraction of opposite charges, + and –).

2) This strong attraction is known as <u>electrostatic attraction</u> — it gives ionic compounds their <u>high melting</u> and <u>boiling points</u>.

> **When an atom <u>loses electrons</u>, it's called <u>OXIDATION</u>.**
> **When an atom <u>gains electrons</u>, it's called <u>REDUCTION</u>.**

A Shell with Just **One** *Electron is* **Well Keen to Get Rid**

1) <u>All</u> the atoms over at the <u>left-hand side</u> of the periodic table, e.g. <u>sodium, potassium, calcium</u> etc., have just <u>one or two electrons</u> in their outer shell.

2) They're <u>pretty keen to get shot of them</u>, because then they'll only have <u>full shells</u> left, which is how they <u>like</u> it.

3) So given half a chance they do get rid, and that leaves the atom as an <u>ion</u> instead.

4) Now, ions aren't the kind of things that sit around quietly watching the world go by. They tend to <u>leap</u> at the first passing ion with an <u>opposite charge</u> and stick to it like glue.

A **Nearly Full** *Shell is* **Well Keen** *to Get That* **Extra Electron**

1) On the <u>other side</u> of the periodic table, the elements in <u>Group 6</u> and <u>Group 7</u>, such as <u>oxygen</u> and <u>chlorine</u>, have outer shells which are <u>nearly full</u>.

2) They're obviously pretty keen to <u>gain</u> that <u>extra one or two electrons</u> to fill the shell up.

3) When they do of course they become <u>ions</u> (you know, not the kind of things to sit around) and before you know it they've latched on to the atom (ion) that gave up the electron a moment earlier.

The reaction of sodium and chlorine is a <u>classic case</u>:

The <u>sodium</u> atom <u>gives up</u> its <u>outer electron</u> and becomes an Na⁺ ion.

The <u>chlorine</u> atom has <u>picked up</u> the <u>spare electron</u> and becomes a Cl⁻ ion.

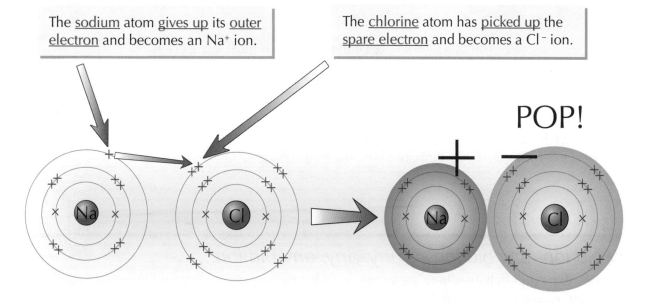

POP!

Ionic Bonding

Elements aren't all as <u>eager</u> as each other to form ions...

Groups *1 & 2* and *6 & 7* are the Most Likely to Form **Ions**

1) The elements that most readily form ions are those in Groups 1, 2, 6 and 7.

2) <u>Group 1 and 2 elements</u> are <u>metals</u> and they <u>lose</u> electrons to form <u>+ve ions</u> (<u>cations</u>).

3) <u>Group 6 and 7 elements</u> are <u>non-metals</u>. They <u>gain</u> electrons to form <u>–ve ions</u> (<u>anions</u>).

4) Make sure you know these easy ones:

<u>Cations</u>		<u>Anions</u>	
<u>Group 1</u>	<u>Group 2</u>	<u>Group 6</u>	<u>Group 7</u>
Li^+	Be^{2+}	O^{2-}	F^-
Na^+	Mg^{2+}	S^{2-}	Cl^-
K^+	Ca^{2+}		Br^-

5) When any of these cations <u>meet up</u> with any of the anions, they attract each other to form an <u>ionic compound</u>.

6) Only elements at <u>opposite sides</u> of the periodic table will form ionic compounds, e.g. Na and Cl, where one of them becomes a <u>cation</u> (+ve) and one becomes an <u>anion</u> (–ve).

7) You <u>don't</u> have to <u>remember</u> what ions <u>most elements</u> form — nope, you just look at the periodic table.

8) Elements in the same <u>group</u> all have the same number of <u>outer electrons</u>. So they have to <u>lose or gain</u> the same number to get a full outer shell. And this means that they form ions with the <u>same charges</u>.

Any old ion, any old ion — any, any, any old ion...

Remember, the + and – charges here are telling you <u>what type of ion</u> the atom will form in a chemical reaction. For example, sodium <u>metal</u> is made up of <u>neutral sodium atoms</u> (<u>Na</u>). They will only become <u>sodium ions</u> (<u>Na⁺</u>) if the sodium metal <u>reacts</u> with something — like water or chlorine.

Ionic Compounds

Make sure you've really got your head around the idea of ionic bonding before you start on this page.

Ionic Compounds All Form in a Similar Way

'Dot and cross' diagrams show what happens to the electrons when ionic bonding happens:

Sodium Chloride (NaCl)

The sodium atom gives up its outer electron, becoming an Na^+ ion. The chlorine atom picks up the electron, becoming a Cl^- (chloride) ion.

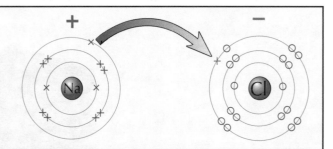

Magnesium Oxide (MgO)

The magnesium atom gives up its two outer electrons, becoming an Mg^{2+} ion. The oxygen atom picks up the electrons, becoming an O^{2-} (oxide) ion.

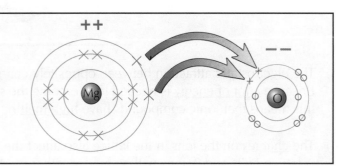

Sodium Oxide (Na₂O)

Two sodium atoms give up their outer electrons, becoming two Na^+ ions. The oxygen atom picks up the two electrons, becoming an O^{2-} ion.

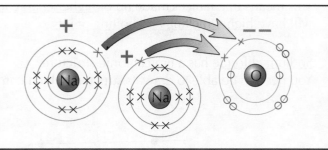

Calcium Chloride (CaCl₂)

The calcium atom gives up its two outer electrons, becoming a Ca^{2+} ion. The two chlorine atoms pick up one electron each, becoming two Cl^- (chloride) ions.

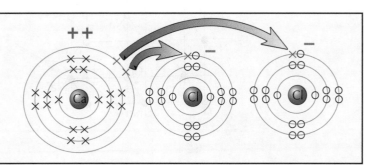

Notice that all the atoms end up with full outer shells
as a result of this giving and taking of electrons.

Ionic Compounds

Giant Ionic Structures Have High Melting and Boiling Points

1) Compounds with <u>ionic bonding</u> always have <u>giant ionic structures</u>.

2) The ions are held together in a <u>closely packed</u> 3D lattice arrangement by the attraction between oppositely charged ions.

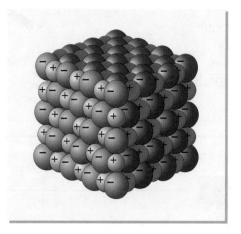

3) The electrostatic attraction between oppositely charged ions is <u>very strong</u>. Because <u>a lot of energy</u> is needed to overcome the strong attraction, this means that ionic compounds have <u>high melting</u> and <u>boiling points</u>.

4) The <u>charges</u> on the ions in the lattice also affect the <u>strength</u> of the ionic bonding. A lattice of 2^+ and 2^- ions will be held together by <u>stronger forces of attraction</u> than a lattice of 1^+ and 1^- ions.

5) This means that lattices made up of <u>higher charge ions</u> will have <u>higher melting and boiling points</u>.

6) <u>Sodium chloride</u> has a typical ionic structure. You need to be able to draw its structure which can be represented like this:

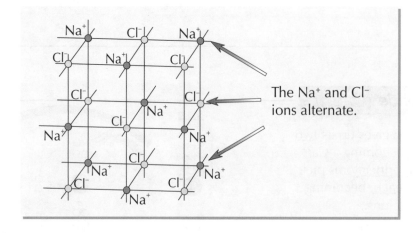

The Na^+ and Cl^- ions alternate.

Ionic compounds are always giant ionic lattices...

...this is because of the attraction between oppositely charged ions. Luckily you only need to be able to draw the structure of one of these — sodium chloride. Make sure you know what it looks like.

Warm-Up and Exam Questions

This stuff's pretty fundamental to Chemistry — so these two pages will check you've got it all learnt.

Warm-Up Questions

1) How many electrons can be held in: a) the first electron shell? b) the second electron shell?
2) What name is given to the type of reaction in which an atom gains electrons?
3) Do elements from Group 1 form positive or negative ions?
4) Do elements from Group 7 form positive or negative ions?

Exam Questions

1   The periodic table contains all the elements arranged in order.

   a)   How are the elements arranged in the periodic table?
        Choose your answer from the options below.

        No of protons

        By atomic number   By electron number

        By mass number   By neutron number
        ↗ protons + neutrons.
                                                              (1 mark)

   b)   How can you deduce the number of electrons in the outer shell of an element from
        its position in the periodic table?
                                                              (1 mark)

2   Beryllium and calcium are both Group 2 elements.

   a)   Give the electronic configuration of beryllium.
                                                              (1 mark)

   b)   The diagram shows the incomplete electron arrangement of a calcium atom.
        Copy and complete the diagram to show the electron arrangement of a calcium atom.

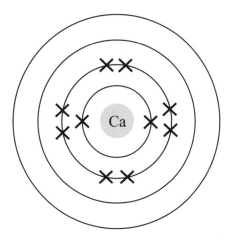

                                                              (2 marks)

   c)   Calcium can react with oxygen to produce calcium oxide.
        How many extra electrons does an atom of oxygen need to fill up its outer shell?
                                                              (1 mark)

Exam Questions

3   Magnesium reacts with sulfur to produce magnesium sulfide.

   a)   In this reaction, magnesium atoms become magnesium ions.
        State what happens when magnesium ions are formed, in terms of loss or gain of
        electrons. Give the name for this type of reaction.

                                                                              (2 marks)

   b)   When they react with sodium, sulfur atoms each gain two electrons. When chlorine
        atoms react with sodium, they each gain only one electron. Explain this difference.

                                                                              (2 marks)

4   Sodium chloride is an ionic compound.

   a)   Copy and complete the sentences below, using words from the box.
        Each word may be used once, more than once, or not at all.

strong   negative   large   positive   weak   high   low   small

        Sodium chloride has very .... electrostatic forces of attraction between
        the .... sodium ions and the .... chloride ions.
        This means that it needs a .... amount of energy to break the bonds,
        and so its melting point is ....

                                                                              (5 marks)

   b)   Draw a dot and cross diagram for the ions in sodium chloride, including the charge
        on each ion. Only show the outer electrons.

                                                                              (3 marks)

PAPER 2

5   Different compounds have different melting points.

   a)   Sodium chloride and magnesium oxide are both ionic compounds.
        State which compound you would expect to have
        a higher melting point, and explain your answer.

                                                                              (3 marks)

   b)   The melting point of sodium chloride is related to its structure.

        i)   Briefly describe the structure of sodium chloride and how it is held together.

                                                                              (2 marks)

        ii)   Which of the diagrams **A**, **B** or **C** correctly represents
              the structure of sodium chloride?

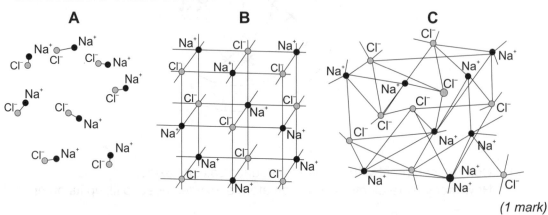

                                                                              (1 mark)

Covalent Bonding

Ionic bonding (see page 19) isn't the only kind of bonding you need to know about — there's <u>covalent bonding</u> too. This is where atoms <u>share electrons</u> with each other so that they've got <u>full outer shells</u>.

A **Covalent** Bond is a **Shared Pair of Electrons**

1) Sometimes atoms prefer to make <u>covalent bonds</u> by <u>sharing</u> pairs of electrons with other atoms.

2) This way <u>both</u> atoms feel that they have a <u>full outer shell</u>, and that makes them happy.

3) Each <u>covalent bond</u> provides one <u>extra</u> shared electron for each atom.

4) Each atom involved has to make <u>enough</u> covalent bonds to <u>fill up</u> its outer shell.

5) In covalent bonding, there's a <u>strong attraction</u> between the <u>shared electrons</u> (the bonding pair) and the <u>nuclei</u> of the atoms involved.

<u>Learn</u> these <u>important examples</u>:

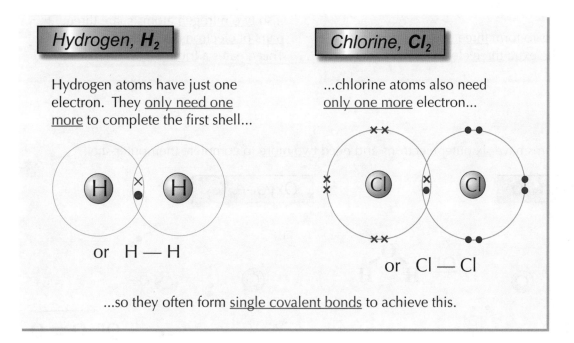

Hydrogen, **H₂**

Hydrogen atoms have just one electron. They <u>only need one more</u> to complete the first shell...

or   H — H

Chlorine, **Cl₂**

...chlorine atoms also need <u>only one more</u> electron...

or   Cl — Cl

...so they often form <u>single covalent bonds</u> to achieve this.

Hydrogen Chloride, **HCl**

This is very similar to H₂ and Cl₂. Again, both atoms <u>only need one more electron</u> to complete their outer shells.

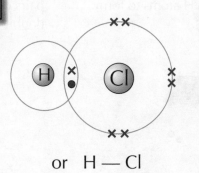

or   H — Cl

In a dot and cross diagram, you only have to draw the outer shell of electrons.

Covalent bonding — it's good to share...

There are more pages of covalent bonding diagrams to come, so make sure you can draw the <u>ones</u> on this page first. When you've drawn a dot and cross diagram, it's a good idea to count up the number of electrons, just to <u>double-check</u> you've got <u>the right number</u> in the outer shell.

Covalent Bonding

Ammonia, NH_3

Nitrogen has <u>five</u> outer electrons...

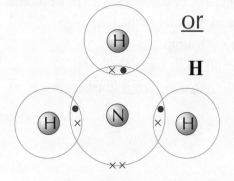

...so it needs to form <u>three covalent bonds</u> to make up the extra <u>three</u> electrons needed.

Nitrogen, N_2

Nitrogen atoms need <u>three more</u> electrons...

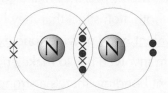

or $N \equiv N$

...so <u>two nitrogen atoms</u> share <u>three pairs of electrons</u> to fill their outer shells. This creates a <u>triple bond</u>.

<u>Oxygen</u> atoms have <u>six</u> outer electrons and need <u>two more</u> to complete their outer shell.

Water, H_2O

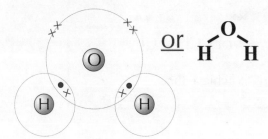

In <u>water molecules</u>, the oxygen shares a pair of electrons with two H atoms to form two <u>single covalent bonds</u>.

Oxygen, O_2

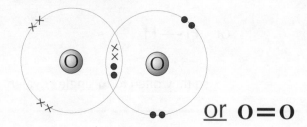

or $O = O$

In <u>oxygen gas</u> one oxygen atom shares two pairs of electrons with another to form a <u>double covalent bond</u>.

Carbon Dioxide, CO_2

In <u>carbon dioxide</u> two oxygen atoms share two pairs of electrons with a carbon atom to form <u>two double covalent bonds</u>.

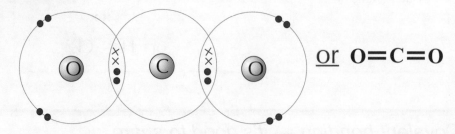

or $O = C = O$

Covalent Bonding

Methane, CH₄

Carbon has <u>four outer electrons</u>, which is <u>half a full</u> shell.

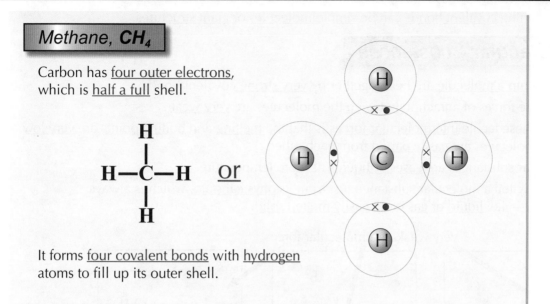

It forms <u>four covalent bonds</u> with <u>hydrogen</u> atoms to fill up its outer shell.

Ethane, C₂H₆

In <u>ethane</u>, 6 <u>hydrogen</u> atoms each share their only electron with one of two carbon atoms.
The two carbon atoms then share their last electrons with <u>each other</u> in a <u>single covalent bond</u>.

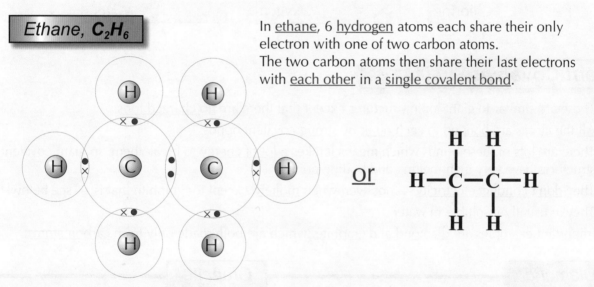

Ethene, C₂H₄

In <u>ethene</u>, 4 hydrogen atoms each share their only electron with one of two carbon atoms. The two carbon atoms then share their last <u>two</u> electrons with each other to form a <u>carbon-carbon double bond</u>.

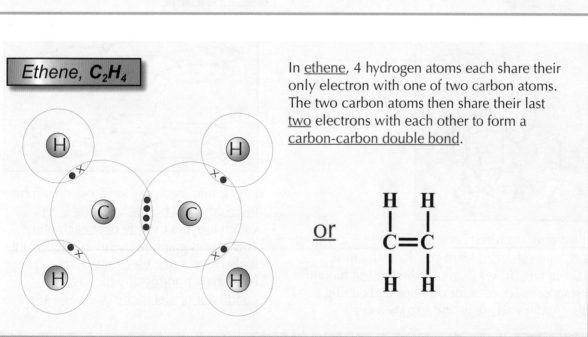

Covalent Substances

Substances containing <u>covalent bonds</u> can be <u>simple molecules</u> or <u>giant structures</u>.

Simple *Molecular* Substances

1) The atoms <u>within a molecule</u> are held together by <u>very strong</u> covalent bonds.

2) By contrast, the forces of attraction <u>between</u> the molecules are <u>very weak</u>.

3) The result of these feeble <u>intermolecular forces</u> is that the <u>melting</u> and <u>boiling points</u> are <u>very low</u>, because the molecules are <u>easily parted</u> from each other.

4) Most molecular substances are <u>gases or liquids</u> at room temperature.

5) You can usually tell a molecular substance just from its <u>physical state</u>, which is always kinda '<u>mushy</u>' — i.e. <u>liquid</u> or <u>gas</u> or an <u>easily melted solid</u>.

Very weak intermolecular forces

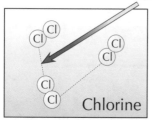
Chlorine

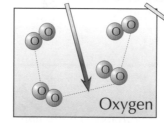
Oxygen

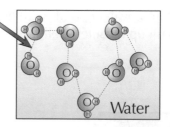
Water

Giant Covalent *Structures*

1) These are similar to giant ionic structures except that there are <u>no charged ions</u>.

2) <u>All</u> the atoms are <u>bonded</u> to <u>each other</u> by <u>strong</u> covalent bonds.

3) There are <u>lots</u> of these bonds which means it takes a <u>lot of energy</u> to break them, so giant covalent structures have <u>very high</u> melting and boiling points.

4) They <u>don't conduct electricity</u> — not even when <u>molten</u> (except for graphite that is — see below).

5) They're usually <u>insoluble</u> in water.

6) Important examples are <u>diamond</u> and <u>graphite</u>, which are both made only from <u>carbon atoms</u>.

Diamond

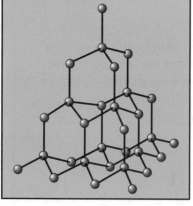

You need to be able to draw these structures.

In diamond, each carbon atom forms <u>four covalent bonds</u> in a <u>very rigid</u> giant covalent structure. This structure makes diamond the <u>hardest</u> natural substance, so it's used for drill tips and cutting tools. And it's all <u>pretty</u> and <u>sparkly</u> too.

Graphite

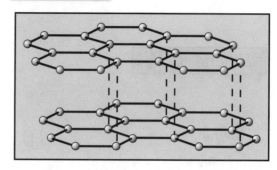

In graphite, each carbon atom only forms <u>three covalent bonds</u>, creating <u>layers</u> which are free to <u>slide over each other</u>. This makes graphite useful as a <u>lubricant</u>. It also leaves <u>free electrons</u>, so graphite is the only <u>non-metal</u> which is a <u>good conductor of electricity</u> (see page 46).

Paper 2   Paper 2   Paper 2   Paper 2

Warm-Up and Exam Questions

Covalent bonding is a mega-important topic. Test your understanding by doing these questions.

Warm-Up Questions

1) How is covalent bonding different from ionic bonding?
2) Why does chlorine have a very low melting point?

Exam Questions

1 Dot and cross diagrams can be used to show the position of electrons in covalent molecules.

   a) Draw dot and cross diagrams for the molecules below.
      Only show the outer electrons.

      i) hydrogen chloride, HCl

(1 mark)

      ii) oxygen, O_2

(1 mark)

      iii) ammonia, NH_3

(1 mark)

   b) Explain how the atoms are held together in a molecule of hydrogen chloride.

(2 marks)

2 Silicon carbide has a giant covalent structure and is a solid at room temperature.
Explain, in terms of its bonding and structure, why silicon carbide has a high melting point.

(2 marks)

PAPER 2

3 Graphite and diamond are both entirely made from carbon, but have different properties.

   a) Why does the structure of graphite make it a useful lubricant?

(2 marks)

   b) Explain why diamond's structure makes it useful as a cutting tool.

(2 marks)

   c) The diagrams below show the arrangement of atoms in four molecules.

A   B   C   D

 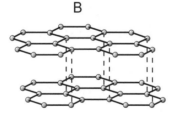 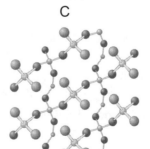 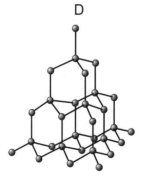

      Choose from the letters **A-D** to answer the questions below.

      i) Which diagram shows the arrangement of atoms in graphite?

(1 mark)

      ii) Which diagram shows the arrangement of atoms in diamond?

(1 mark)

Revision Summary for Section 1 — 1

These certainly aren't the easiest questions you're going to come across. That's because they test what you know without giving you any clues. At first you might think they're impossibly difficult. Eventually you'll realise that they simply test whether you've learnt the stuff or not.

If you're struggling to answer these then you need to do some serious learning.

1) A substance keeps the same volume, but changes its shape according to the container it's in. Is it a solid, a liquid or a gas?

2) Are the forces of attraction between the particles in a liquid stronger or weaker than those in a gas?

3) Describe what happens when a substance changes from a liquid to a gas.

✱4) What is diffusion?

✱5) Describe an experiment that you can do to demonstrate diffusion. *Bromine gas + air*

6) Sketch the nuclear model of an atom.
Give three details about the nucleus and three details about the electrons.

7) Draw a table showing the relative masses and charges of the three types of particle in an atom.

8) What do the mass number and atomic number of an element tell you?

9) Describe the difference between a mixture and a compound.

10)* Say which of the diagrams on the right shows:
   a) a mixture of compounds,
   b) a mixture of elements,
   c) an element,
   d) a compound.

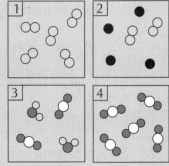

11)* Name the physical method you could use to separate these mixtures:
   a) a mixture of liquids with different boiling points.
   b) an insoluble solid mixed with a liquid.

12) Describe how you could separate the dyes in some inks using paper chromatography.

13) What feature of atoms determines the order of the modern periodic table?

14) How many electrons are in the outer shell of an atom of a Group 7 element?

15) Describe how you would work out the electronic configuration of an atom, given its atomic number.

16)* Write out the electronic configuration of potassium.
   (Use the periodic table on the inside of the front cover to help.)

17) Describe the process of ionic bonding.

18) Draw a dot and cross diagram to show the bonding in sodium chloride (NaCl).

19) What effect does the charge on the ions have on the melting point of an ionic compound?

20) What is covalent bonding?

21) Sketch dot and cross diagrams showing the bonding in molecules of:
   a) hydrogen, b) chlorine, c) water, d) carbon dioxide, e) ethene.

22) a) Describe one property of simple molecular substances.
   b) Explain how the bonding in simple molecular substances causes this property.

23) Describe and explain the differences between the physical properties of simple molecular substances and giant covalent substances.

*Answers on page 190.

Balancing Equations

Equations show you what's happening in a chemical reaction — what <u>reacts together</u> and what's <u>formed</u>.

Equations Show the Reactants and Products of a Reaction

A chemical reaction can be described as the process of going from REACTANTS to PRODUCTS.

You can write <u>word equations</u> or <u>symbol equations</u> to show any chemical reaction.

e.g. magnesium reacts with oxygen to produce magnesium oxide:

Word equation: magnesium + oxygen → magnesium oxide
Symbol equation: $2Mg + O_2 → 2MgO$

Look out for <u>state symbols</u> in equations — they tell you
what <u>physical state</u> the reactants and products are in:

(s) — Solid　　　**(l) — Liquid**　　　**(g) — Gas**　　　**(aq) — Aqueous (dissolved in water)**

Here's the example with the state symbols in: $2Mg(s) + O_2(g) → 2MgO(s)$ ← *So, this is solid magnesium reacting with oxygen gas to make solid magnesium oxide.*

Symbol Equations Need to Be Balanced

1) There must always be the <u>same</u> number of atoms on <u>both sides</u> — they can't just <u>disappear</u>.
2) You <u>balance</u> symbol equations by putting numbers <u>in front</u> of the formulae where needed.

Take this equation for burning propane in oxygen to make carbon dioxide and water:

$$C_3H_8 + O_2 → CO_2 + H_2O$$

The <u>formulae</u> are all correct but the numbers of some atoms <u>don't match up</u> on both sides.
E.g. there are <u>three</u> carbon atoms on the left-hand side, but there's only <u>one</u> on the right-hand side.
You <u>can't change formulae</u>, like C_3H_8 to CH_8. You can only put numbers <u>in front of them</u>:

Method: Balance just ONE type of atom at a time

The more you practise, the quicker you'll get, but all you do is this:

1) Find an element that <u>doesn't balance</u> and <u>pencil in a number</u> to try and sort it out.
2) <u>See where it gets you</u>. It may create <u>another imbalance</u>, but pencil in <u>another number</u> and see where that gets you.
3) Carry on chasing <u>unbalanced</u> elements and it'll <u>sort itself out</u> pretty quickly.

<u>I'll show you</u>. In the equation above you soon notice
we're short of H atoms on the RHS (right-hand side).

1) The only thing you can do about that is make it $4H_2O$ instead of just H_2O:
$$C_3H_8 + O_2 → CO_2 + 4H_2O$$

2) We're also short of C atoms on the RHS, so to balance that up change CO_2 to $3CO_2$:
$$C_3H_8 + O_2 → 3CO_2 + 4H_2O$$

3) Now the O atoms are out of balance.
You can sort that out by making it $5O_2$ on the left-hand side:
$$C_3H_8 + 5O_2 → 3CO_2 + 4H_2O$$

4) And suddenly there it is. <u>Everything balances</u>.

Isotopes

Some elements have more than one isotope. "But what's an isotope?" I hear you cry. Read on...

Isotopes are the Same Except for an Extra **Neutron** or Two

A favourite exam question is: "Explain the meaning of the term isotope"
The trick is that it's impossible to explain what one isotope is. Nice of them that, isn't it!
You have to outsmart them and always start your answer "Isotopes are..." LEARN the definition:

> **Isotopes are: different atomic forms of the same element, which have the SAME number of PROTONS but a DIFFERENT number of NEUTRONS.**

1) The upshot is: isotopes must have the same proton number but different mass numbers.

2) If they had different proton numbers, they'd be different elements altogether.

3) A very popular pair of isotopes are carbon-12 and carbon-14, used for carbon dating.

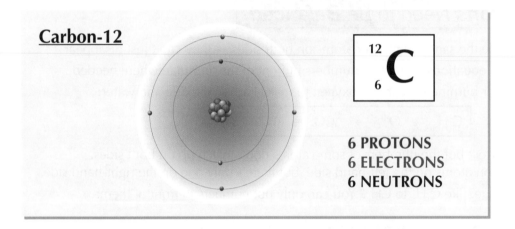

Carbon-12

$^{12}_{6}\text{C}$

6 PROTONS
6 ELECTRONS
6 NEUTRONS

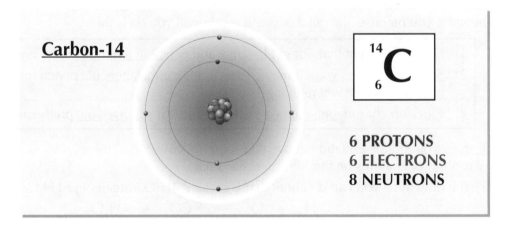

Carbon-14

$^{14}_{6}\text{C}$

6 PROTONS
6 ELECTRONS
8 NEUTRONS

Will this be in your exam — isotope so...

Carbon-14 is unstable. It makes up about one ten-millionth of the carbon in living things. When things die, the C-14 is trapped inside the dead material, and it gradually decays into nitrogen. So by measuring the proportion of C-14 found in some old wood you can calculate how long ago it was living wood.

Relative Atomic Mass

Relative atomic mass isn't as bad as it sounds, I promise. Come on, let's take a look...

Relative Atomic Mass Takes All Stable Isotopes into Account

1) Relative atomic mass (A_r) is just a way of saying how heavy different atoms are compared with the mass of an atom of carbon-12. So carbon-12 has an A_r of exactly 12.

2) It's the average mass of all the isotopes of an element. It has to allow for the relative mass of each isotope and its relative abundance.

3) Relative abundance just means how much there is of each isotope compared to the total amount of the element in the world. This can be a ratio, a fraction or a percentage.

Example: Work out the relative atomic mass of chlorine.

element	relative mass of isotope	relative abundance
chlorine	35	3
	37	1

This means that there are 2 isotopes of chlorine. One has a relative mass of 35 (^{35}Cl) and the other 37 (^{37}Cl).

The relative abundances show that there are 3 atoms of ^{35}Cl to every 1 of ^{37}Cl.

1) Multiply the mass of each isotope by its relative abundance.
2) Add those together.
3) Divide by the sum of the relative abundances.

$$A_r = \frac{(35 \times 3) + (37 \times 1)}{3 + 1} = \underline{35.5}$$

---

4) You can find the relative atomic mass of any element using the periodic table (see the inside of the front cover).

5) Relative atomic masses don't usually come out as whole numbers or easy decimals, but they're often rounded to the nearest 0.5 in periodic tables.

It's relatively simple once you get your head around it...

Fans of statistics will recognise the formula for working out relative atomic mass as a simple weighted average. Just remember which numbers go where and you'll be able to do these in your sleep.

Relative Formula Mass

The biggest trouble with <u>relative formula mass</u> is that it <u>sounds</u> so blood-curdling.
It's very important though, so take a few deep breaths, and just enjoy, as the mists slowly clear...

Relative Formula Mass, M_r

If you have a compound like $MgCl_2$ then it has a <u>relative formula mass</u>, M_r, which is just all the relative
atomic masses (see page 33) of the atoms it contains <u>added together</u>.

For $MgCl_2$ it would be:

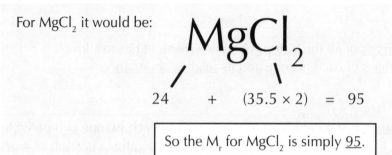

$$24 \quad + \quad (35.5 \times 2) \quad = \quad 95$$

So the M_r for $MgCl_2$ is simply <u>95</u>.

You can easily get the A_r for any element from the <u>periodic table</u>.
In the exam you'll be given a periodic table so you can look them up.

I'll tell you what, since it's nearly Christmas I'll run through a couple more examples for you:

What's the relative formula mass of KNO_3?

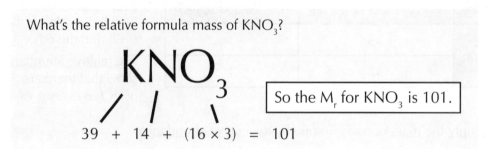

$$39 \quad + \quad 14 \quad + \quad (16 \times 3) \quad = \quad 101$$

So the M_r for KNO_3 is 101.

QUESTION: Find the relative formula mass for the alcohol $C_2H_4(OH)_2$,
using the given data:

A_r for C = 12 A_r for H = 1 A_r for O = 16

ANSWER:

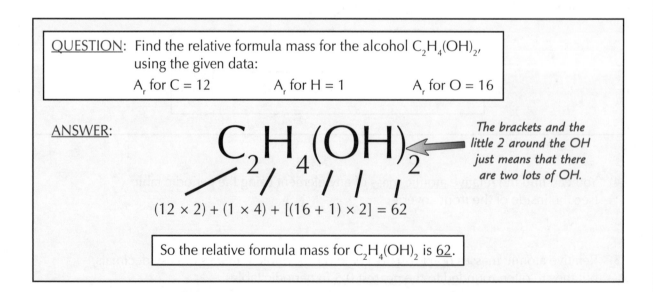

The brackets and the little 2 around the OH just means that there are two lots of OH.

$$(12 \times 2) + (1 \times 4) + [(16 + 1) \times 2] = 62$$

So the relative formula mass for $C_2H_4(OH)_2$ is <u>62</u>.

Just add up the masses and watch out for brackets...

And that's all it is. A big fancy name like <u>relative formula mass</u> and all it means is "<u>add up all the mass
numbers</u>". What a swizz, eh? Still, that's life — it's all a big disappointment in the end. Sigh.

Empirical and Molecular Formula

Finding the **Empirical Formula** (from Masses or Percentages)

1) The empirical formula gives you the smallest whole-number ratio of atoms in a compound.

2) Try this for an easy peasy stepwise method for calculating an empirical formula:

    1) List all the elements in the compound (there are usually only two or three).

    2) Underneath them, write their experimental masses or percentages.

    3) Divide each mass or percentage by the relative atomic mass (A_r) for that particular element.

    4) Turn the numbers you get into a nice simple ratio by multiplying and/or dividing them by well-chosen numbers.

    5) Get the ratio in its simplest form — that tells you the empirical formula of the compound.

Example: In an experiment, some iron oxide powder is reduced to pure metallic iron. Use the following experimental data to find the empirical formula of the iron oxide used.

Mass of empty container	32.0 g
Mass of container + mass of iron oxide	96.0 g
Mass of container + iron	76.8 g

(A_r for iron = 56, A_r for oxygen = 16)

Method:

During the experiment oxygen is lost. The mass of oxygen lost is the difference between the mass of the container and iron oxide and the mass of the container and iron: 96.0 g − 76.8 g = 19.2 g.

The mass of iron made is the difference between the mass of the container with the iron and the mass of the empty container: 76.8 g − 32.0 g = 44.8 g.

1) List the two elements: Fe   O

2) Write in the experimental masses: 44.8   19.2

3) Divide by the A_r for each element: 44.8 ÷ 56 = 0.8   19.2 ÷ 16 = 1.2

4) Multiply by 10...   8   12

5) ...then divide by 4:   2   3

So the simplest formula is 2 atoms of Fe to 3 atoms of O, i.e. Fe_2O_3. And that's it done.

Empirical and **Molecular Formulae** aren't Always the Same

The EMPIRICAL FORMULA of a compound is the simplest formula that tells you the ratio of different elements in the compound.
The MOLECULAR FORMULA of a compound tells you the actual number of atoms of each element in a single molecule.

Molecular formulae are whole-number multiples of empirical formulae.

Example: A molecule has an empirical formula of $C_4H_3O_2$, and a relative molecular mass of 166. Work out its molecular formula.

Method: 1) Find the mass of the empirical formula: $(4 \times 12) + (3 \times 1) + (2 \times 16) = 48 + 3 + 32 = 83$ g

        2) The relative molecular mass is 166, so there are 166 ÷ 83 = 2 empirical units in the molecule.

        3) The molecular formula must be the empirical formula × 2, so the molecular formula must be $C_4H_3O_2 \times 2 = C_8H_6O_4$. So there you go.

Calculating Masses in Reactions

These can be kinda scary, but chill out, little trembling one — just relax and enjoy.

The Three Important Steps — *Not to be Missed...*

1) Write out the <u>balanced equation</u>.

2) For the two bits you want, <u>work out the relative formula mass</u> (M_r) and <u>multiply them</u> by the <u>balancing numbers</u> in the equation.

3) Apply the rule: <u>Divide to get one, then multiply to get all</u>. (But you have to apply this first to the substance they give information about, and then the other one!)

Don't worry — these steps should all make sense when you look at the example below.

<u>EXAMPLE:</u> What mass of magnesium oxide is produced when 60 g of magnesium is burnt in air?

1) Write out the <u>balanced equation</u>: $2Mg + O_2 \rightarrow 2MgO$

2) Work out the <u>relative formula masses</u> of the two bits you want and multiply them by the balancing numbers in the equation:
$$2Mg: 2 \times 24 = 48 \qquad 2MgO: 2 \times (24 + 16) = 80$$

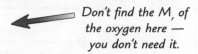 *Don't find the M_r of the oxygen here — you don't need it.*

3) Apply the rule: <u>Divide to get one, then multiply to get all</u>.
The two numbers, 48 and 80, tell us that <u>48 g of Mg</u> react to give <u>80 g of MgO</u>.
Here's the tricky bit. We need to find out what happens when <u>60 g of Mg</u> is burnt in air.

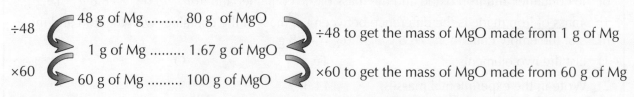

$\div48$ 48 g of Mg .... 80 g of MgO $\div48$ to get the mass of MgO made from 1 g of Mg

1 g of Mg .... 1.67 g of MgO

$\times60$ 60 g of Mg .... 100 g of MgO $\times60$ to get the mass of MgO made from 60 g of Mg

This tells us that <u>60 g of magnesium</u> will produce <u>100 g of magnesium oxide</u>.
If the question had said, "<u>Find how much magnesium</u> gives 500 g of magnesium oxide", you'd fill in the <u>MgO side first</u>, because that's the one you'd have the information about. Got it? Good-O!

The mass of product (in this case magnesium oxide) is called the <u>yield</u> of a reaction. Masses you calculate in this way are called <u>theoretical yields</u>. In practice you never get 100% of the yield, so the amount of product you get will be <u>less</u> than you calculated.

Percentage Yield Compares *Actual* and *Theoretical* Yield

The more reactant you start with, the higher the <u>yield</u> will be — that's pretty obvious.
But the <u>percentage yield</u> doesn't depend on the <u>amount</u> of reactants you started with — it's a <u>percentage</u>.

1) The <u>theoretical yield</u> of a reaction can be calculated from the <u>balanced equation</u> (see above).

2) Percentage yield is given by the formula:

$$\text{percentage yield} = \frac{\text{actual yield (grams)}}{\text{theoretical yield (grams)}} \times 100$$

3) Percentage yield is <u>always</u> somewhere between 0 and 100%.

4) A 100% yield means that you got <u>all</u> the product you expected to get.

5) A 0% yield means that <u>no</u> reactants were converted into product, i.e. no product at all was <u>made</u>.

Paper 2

Warm-Up and Exam Questions

There's only one way to get good at these — build an automatic formula mass calculating machine. Just kidding, you've got to work through these questions. Not as fun, but certainly more effective.

Warm-Up Questions

1) What name is given to the average mass of isotopes of an element?
2) What name is given to the sum of the relative atomic masses of atoms in a molecule?
3) What is the formula for calculating the percentage yield of a reaction?

Exam Questions

1   Methane (CH_4) burns in oxygen (O_2) to make carbon dioxide (CO_2) and water (H_2O).
   a)   State the names of the reactants and products in this reaction.

(2 marks)

   b)   Write a word equation for this reaction.

(1 mark)

   c)   Write a balanced chemical equation for this reaction.

(2 marks)

2   Two of the most common isotopes of chlorine are chlorine-35 (^{35}Cl) and chlorine-37 (^{37}Cl).
   a)   State what is meant by the term isotope.

(2 marks)

   b)   Copy and complete the following table to show the mass number and the numbers of protons and neutrons in each of these chlorine isotopes.

Isotope	Mass number	Number of protons	Number of neutrons
^{35}Cl	35	17	
^{37}Cl			

(2 marks)

   c)   The relative abundances of ^{35}Cl and ^{37}Cl are shown in the table below.

Isotope	Relative abundance
^{35}Cl	75%
^{37}Cl	25%

   i)   What is meant by the term **relative atomic mass**?

(2 marks)

   ii)   Use the information in the table to work out the relative atomic mass of chlorine.

(3 marks)

3   A solution of calcium hydroxide, $Ca(OH)_2$ can be known as limewater.
   Calculate the relative formula mass of calcium hydroxide, $Ca(OH)_2$.

(2 marks)

Exam Questions

4   Nitrogen monoxide, NO, reacts with oxygen, O_2, to form oxide R.
    A 100 g sample of oxide R contains 30.4 g of nitrogen and 69.6 g of oxygen.
    Work out the empirical formula of oxide R.

(3 marks)

5   A molecule has an empirical formula of C_3H_7O, and a relative molecular mass of 118.
    Deduce the molecular formula of the molecule.

(3 marks)

6   A student is investigating the combustion of metals.

    a)   The student burns 10 g of magnesium in air to produce magnesium oxide (MgO).

    $$2Mg + O_2 \rightarrow 2MgO$$

    Calculate the maximum mass of magnesium oxide that could be
    produced in the reaction. Give your answer in grams.

(3 marks)

    b)   Using the chemical equation below, work out the mass of sodium that the
    student would need to burn in order to produce 2 g of sodium oxide.
    Give your answer in grams.

    $$4Na + O_2 \rightarrow 2Na_2O$$

(3 marks)

PAPER 2

7   Solutions of barium chloride and sodium sulfate were mixed together in a beaker
    to produce barium sulfate. The solution was filtered to obtain the solid barium sulfate.
    The reaction was predicted to give a yield of 15 g of barium sulfate.
    However, after the experiment was completed a yield of only 6 g had been obtained.
    Calculate the percentage yield.

(1 mark)

PAPER 2

8   The reaction between magnesium and oxygen produces a white powder, magnesium oxide.
    Three samples of magnesium, each weighing 2 g, were burned and the oxide produced was
    weighed. The expected yield was 3.33 g.
    Copy and complete the following table with the percentage yields of the three samples.

Sample	Mass of oxide (g)	Percentage yield
A	3.18	
B	3.05	
C	3.15	

(3 marks)

Moles

The mole is really confusing. I think it's the word that puts people off. It's very difficult to see the relevance of the word "mole" to anything but a small burrowing animal.

"The Mole" is Simply the Name Given to a Certain Number

1) Just like "a million" is this many: 1 000 000; or "a billion" is this many: 1 000 000 000, so "a mole" is this many: 602 300 000 000 000 000 000 000 or 6.023×10^{23}.

2) And that's all it is. Just a number. The burning question, of course, is why is it such a silly long one like that, and with a six at the front?

3) The answer is that when you get precisely that number of atoms or molecules, of any element or compound, then, conveniently, they weigh exactly the same number of grams as the relative atomic mass, A_r (or relative formula mass, M_r) of the element or compound. This is arranged on purpose, of course, to make things easier.

4) One mole of atoms or molecules of any substance will have a mass in grams equal to the relative formula mass (A_r or M_r) for that substance.

> **Examples**
>
> Carbon has an A_r of 12.   So one mole of carbon weighs exactly 12 g.
> Nitrogen gas, N_2, has an M_r of 28 (2×14).   So one mole of N_2 weighs exactly 28 g.
> Carbon dioxide, CO_2, has an M_r of 44.   So one mole of CO_2 weighs exactly 44 g.

5) This means that 12 g of carbon, or 28 g of N_2, or 44 g of CO_2, all contain the same number of particles, namely one mole or 6.023×10^{23} atoms or molecules.

6) The molar mass of a substance is just another way of saying 'the mass of one mole'. Molar mass is measured in grams too. E.g. the molar mass of carbon is 12 g.

Avogadro's Number

The number 6.023×10^{23} is called Avogadro's number or the Avogadro constant. So you can think of a mole as the Avogadro number of particles in a substance, where the particles are atoms, molecules, ions or electrons.

Easy Formula for Finding the Number of Moles in a Given Mass:

$$\text{Number of moles} = \frac{\text{Mass in g (of element or compound)}}{M_r \text{ (of element or compound)}}$$

Example: How many moles are there in 66 g of carbon dioxide?

Method: M_r of CO_2 = 12 + (16 × 2) = 44
         No. of moles = Mass (g) ÷ M_r = 66 ÷ 44 = 1.5 moles. Easy Peasy.

Get that formula learnt...

Moles can definitely be a bit confusing. You need to be able to convert between moles and grams for the exam though — so spend a bit of time getting your head round all this if you need to.

Paper 2

Water of Crystallisation

Some salts are <u>hydrated</u> — their lattices contain <u>water molecules</u> as well as positive and negative ions.

Salts Can be *Anhydrous* or *Hydrated*

1) All solid salts consist of a <u>lattice</u> of positive and negative <u>ions</u> (see page 22).

2) In some salts, <u>water molecules</u> are incorporated in the lattice too.

Here's a tiny part of the lattice in a <u>hydrated salt</u>:

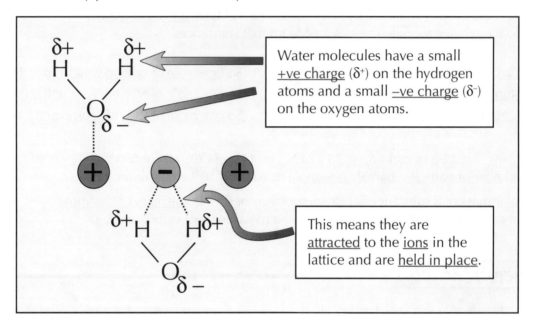

Water molecules have a small <u>+ve charge</u> (δ^+) on the hydrogen atoms and a small <u>–ve charge</u> (δ^-) on the oxygen atoms.

This means they are <u>attracted</u> to the <u>ions</u> in the lattice and are <u>held in place</u>.

3) The water in a lattice is called <u>water of crystallisation</u>.

4) A solid salt containing water of crystallisation is <u>hydrated</u>.

5) If a salt <u>doesn't</u> contain any water of crystallisation, it's called <u>anhydrous</u>.

Hydrated = contains water, anhydrous = doesn't contain water...

Trust chemists to come up with complicated terms for 'contains water' and 'doesn't contain water'.
This page is all pretty straightforward, so make sure you understand it all before you move on.
Next up, there's a little bit of hydrated salt-related maths... What fun.

Water of Crystallisation

Calculating *How Much* **Water of Crystallisation** *a Salt Contains*

1) One mole of a hydrated salt always has a particular number of moles of water of crystallisation — its formula shows how many (it's always a whole number).

2) For example, hydrated copper sulfate has five moles of water for every one mole of the salt. So its formula is $CuSO_4.5H_2O$. (Notice that there's a dot between the $CuSO_4$ and the $5H_2O$.)

3) Many hydrated salts lose their water of crystallisation when heated, to become anhydrous. If you know the mass of the salt when it's hydrated and when it's anhydrous, you can work its formula out like this:

Example: Heating hydrated magnesium sulfate, $MgSO_4.XH_2O$, in a crucible forms anhydrous magnesium sulfate, $MgSO_4$. Use the experimental data below to find the value of X and write the formula of the hydrated salt.

Mass of empty crucible	42.000 g
Mass of crucible + $MgSO_4.XH_2O$	45.210 g
Mass of crucible + $MgSO_4$	43.567 g

Method:
1) First, work out what mass of $MgSO_4.XH_2O$ and $MgSO_4$ you have.
Mass of $MgSO_4.XH_2O$ = 45.210 − 42.000 = 3.210 g
Mass of $MgSO_4$ = 43.567 − 42.000 = 1.567 g

M_r H_2O = (2 × 1) + 16
= 18

2) Calculate the number of moles of water lost.
Mass of water lost: 3.210 − 1.567 = 1.643 g
Number of moles of water lost: mass ÷ M_r = 1.643 g ÷ 18 = 0.0913 moles

3) Calculate the number of moles of anhydrous salt made.
Molar mass of $MgSO_4$: 24 + 32 + (4 × 16) = 120 g/mol
Number of moles $MgSO_4$: mass ÷ M_r = 1.567 ÷ 120 = 0.0131 moles

4) Work out the ratio of moles of anhydrous salt to moles of water.
From the experiment, 0.0131 moles of salt : 0.0913 moles of water,
So, 1 mole of salt : (0.0913 ÷ 0.0131) = 6.97 moles of water

5) X must be a whole number, and some errors are to be expected in any experiment, so you can round off your result — X = 7 and the formula of the hydrated salt is $MgSO_4.7H_2O$.

Practice makes perfect when it comes to this calculation...

This working-out-the-formula business can be a bit tricky to get your head around — but if you follow the same method each time you'll soon work it out. Oh, and don't forget the dot. It's very important.

Calculating Volumes

Run for your lives now, while you've still got the chance — it's <u>equations</u> and stuff.

Avogadro's Law — One Mole of Any Gas Occupies 24 dm³

The space that <u>one mole</u> of a gas takes up is called its <u>molar volume</u>. Here's a handy fact about molar volume that you definitely <u>need to learn</u>:

dm³ is a fancy way of writing 'litre', so 1 dm³ = 1000 cm³

24 dm³ is the <u>molar volume</u> at RTP. ➡

> <u>One mole</u> of <u>any gas</u> always occupies <u>24 dm³</u> (= 24 000 cm³) at room temperature and pressure (RTP: 25 °C and 1 atmosphere)

This means you can use the formulae below to convert the number of moles, or mass, of <u>any</u> gas to a <u>volume</u>:

> **VOLUME (dm³) = moles of gas × 24**

> $$\text{VOLUME (dm}^3) = \frac{\text{mass of gas}}{M_r \text{ of gas}} \times 24$$

<u>Example 1:</u> What's the volume of 4.5 moles of chlorine at RTP?

 Answer: volume of 1 mole = 24 dm³, so volume of 4.5 moles = 4.5 × 24 dm³ = <u>108 dm³</u>

<u>Example 2:</u> How many moles are there in 8280 cm³ of hydrogen gas at RTP?

 Answer: Number of moles = $\dfrac{\text{Volume of gas}}{\text{Volume of 1 mole}}$ = $\dfrac{8.28}{24}$ = <u>0.345 moles</u>

Don't forget to convert from cm³ to dm³.

You Can Calculate Volumes in Reactions If You Know the Masses

For this type of question there are <u>two stages</u>:

1) <u>Find the reacting mass</u>, exactly like in the examples on page 36.

2) Then <u>convert the mass into a volume</u> using the formula above.

<u>Example:</u>   Find the volume of carbon dioxide produced (at room T and P) when 2.7 g of carbon is completely burned in oxygen. (A$_r$ of carbon = 12, A$_r$ of oxygen = 16)

<u>Method:</u>

1) Balanced equation: C + O$_2$ →   CO$_2$

2) Write down the M$_r$ for each: ÷12 ⌇   12   32   44   ⌇ ÷12

3) Divide for one, times for all: 1   ....   3.666...

                                                   ×2.7 ⌇ 2.7   ....   <u>9.9</u>   ⌇ ×2.7

4) So 2.7 g of C gives 9.9 g of CO$_2$.

   Now the new bit:

   <u>Using the above formula:</u> ➡ Volume = $\dfrac{\text{MASS}}{M_r} \times 24$

 so Volume = (MASS/M$_r$) × 24 = (9.9/44) × 24 = <u>5.4 dm³</u>

That's ANY gas — oxygen, methane, carbon dioxide, ANY gas...

All this stuff ties in with page 36 — if you're not comfortable working out the reacting masses have a look there first. The only new thing here is the molar volume business: <u>1 mole of gas = 24 000 cm³</u>.

Moles and Concentration

Concentration is the 'Amount of Stuff' per Unit Volume

1) The <u>concentration</u> of a solution is usually measured in <u>moles per dm³</u> (i.e. <u>moles per litre</u>).
So 1 mole of stuff in 1 dm³ of solution has a concentration of <u>1 mole per dm³</u> (or 1 mol/dm³).

2) You might also sometimes see concentration being measured in <u>grams per dm³</u>. So 56 grams
of stuff dissolved in 1 dm³ of solution has a concentration of <u>56 g per dm³</u> (or 56 g/dm³).

Concentration = No. of Moles ÷ Volume

1) If you ever have to find the <u>concentration</u> of a
solution, here's the <u>formula triangle</u> you'll need:

*Concentration =
No. of moles ÷ Volume*

Concentration
(in mol/dm³)

Number of moles

$$\frac{n}{c \times v}$$

Volume (in dm³)
(One dm³ is a litre.)

> <u>Example 1:</u> What's the concentration of a solution with 2 moles of potassium iodide in 500 cm³?
>
> <u>Answer:</u> Easy — you've got 2 moles of potassium iodide and 500 cm³ = 0.5 dm³.
> So just stick these numbers in the formula: Concentration = 2 ÷ 0.5 = <u>4 mol/dm³</u>

2) You can use the same formula triangle to find the <u>number of moles</u> that are in a solution:

> <u>Example 2:</u> How many moles of sodium chloride are in 250 cm³ of a 3 mol/dm³ solution?
>
> <u>Answer:</u> 250 cm³ = 0.25 dm³. So, using the formula from the triangle...
> Number of moles = concentration × volume = 3 × 0.25 = <u>0.75 moles</u>

Converting Moles per dm³ to Grams per dm³

1) Calculating concentrations in <u>grams per dm³</u> is easy. You just divide the <u>mass</u>
of the chemical in <u>grams</u> by the <u>volume</u> of solvent you used to dissolve it in <u>dm³</u>.

> <u>Example 1:</u> Give the concentration in g/dm³ of a solution made
> by dissolving 3 g of NaCl in 100 cm³ of water.
>
> <u>Answer:</u> Concentration = mass (g) ÷ volume (dm³) = 3 ÷ 0.1 = <u>30 g/dm³</u>

2) Changing a concentration from <u>mol/dm³</u> to <u>g/dm³</u> isn't too tricky.
All you need to do is use the formula you met on page 39
to convert the <u>moles</u> per dm³ into <u>mass</u> per dm³.

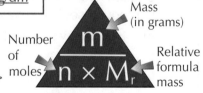

Mass
(in grams)

Number
of
moles

$$\frac{m}{n \times M_r}$$

Relative
formula
mass

> <u>Example 2:</u> You have a 0.04 mol/dm³ solution of sulfuric acid.
> What is the concentration in grams per dm³?
>
> <u>Step 1:</u> Work out the <u>relative formula mass</u> of the chemical.
> So, $H_2SO_4 = (1 \times 2) + 32 + (16 \times 4) = 98$
>
> <u>Step 2:</u> Convert the concentration in <u>moles</u> into concentration in <u>grams</u>.
> So, in 1 dm³: Mass in grams = moles × relative formula mass
> = 0.04 × 98 = 3.92 g
>
> So the <u>concentration in g/dm³ = 3.92 g/dm³</u>

Warm-Up and Exam Questions

There have been plenty of calculations on the last couple of pages. None of them are too bad to get to grips with, but you do have to remember how to do each type. Try these lovely questions:

Warm-Up Questions

1) What is the mass of one mole of iron?
2) What is the name given to the particular number of particles equal to one mole of a substance?

Exam Questions

1   A student was asked to calculate the number of moles and the masses of different compounds she would be using in her lab practical.

a)   State the formula used to work out the number of moles from the mass of a substance.

(1 mark)

b)   Calculate the number of moles in the following substances.
   i)   14 g of lithium
   ii)   112 g of sulfur
   iii)   390 g of silicon dioxide (SiO_2)
   iv)   275 g of zinc carbonate ($ZnCO_3$)

(4 marks)

c)   Calculate the masses of the following molar quantities of substances.
   i)   1 mole of nickel
   ii)   2 moles of aluminium
   iii)   6 moles of hydrochloric acid
   iv)   4.5 moles of copper oxide (CuO)

(4 marks)

2   Sodium hydroxide (NaOH) reacts with sulfuric acid to produce sodium sulfate (Na_2SO_4) and water.

a)   How many moles of sodium hydroxide are in 125 cm^3 of a 2.5 mol/dm^3 solution?

(1 mark)

b)   What is the concentration of a solution with 3 moles of sodium sulfate in 750 cm^3?

(1 mark)

c)   Give your answer for part b) in g/dm^3.

(2 marks)

3   A teacher has a 140 g sample of potassium hydroxide (KOH).
Calculate how much more KOH the teacher needs to have a 4 mole sample.

(2 marks)

Exam Questions

4   $Na_2CO_3.xH_2O$ is a hydrated salt, which means that water molecules are present in the lattice structure. This water is called water of crystallisation.

By heating a sample of a hydrated salt you can gradually remove the water of crystallisation to form an anhydrous salt. This can be done by placing a sample of the hydrated salt into a crucible and gently heating it using a Bunsen burner.

A student used this method to remove the water of crystallisation from $Na_2CO_3.xH_2O$ to produce the anhydrous salt Na_2CO_3. The student put a sample of $Na_2CO_3.xH_2O$ into a crucible, weighed both together, and recorded the mass. The student then heated the sample for 2 minutes, left it to cool and recorded the mass of the sample and crucible again. The student repeated this until two separate masses that had the same value were recorded. The student made a note of this mass.

The student recorded the following masses:

Starting mass of crucible + $Na_2CO_3.xH_2O$	61.224 g
Final mass of crucible + Na_2CO_3	56.364 g

a)   What is the purpose of heating the hydrated salt until the mass remains constant?

(1 mark)

b)   The mass of the crucible was 53.500 g.
     Use this to calculate the masses of the following samples.
     i) $Na_2CO_3.xH_2O$

(1 mark)

     ii) Na_2CO_3

(1 mark)

c)   The relative formula mass of water is 18.

     Calculate the relative formula mass of Na_2CO_3 and use this along with your answers to part b) to work out the value of x in $Na_2CO_3.xH_2O$.

(4 marks)

PAPER 2

5   The volume that one mole of a gas occupies at room temperature and pressure is called its molar volume.
a)   State the value of the molar volume of a gas.

(1 mark)

b)   i)   What volume does 1.5 moles of hydrogen take up?

(1 mark)

     ii) How many moles are there in 2250 cm³ of ammonia (NH_3)?

(1 mark)

c)   Find the volume of carbon dioxide produced (at room temperature and pressure) when 6.9 g of carbon is completely burned in oxygen.

$$C + O_2 \rightarrow CO_2$$

(4 marks)

Electrical Conductivity

Electrical conductivity is all about the <u>movement</u> of electrons or ions.

Electric Current is a Flow of Electrons or Ions

1) <u>Electrons</u> have a <u>negative</u> charge. <u>Ions</u> can have either a <u>negative</u> or a <u>positive</u> charge.

2) Electrons and ions can act as <u>charge carriers</u> — they can move charge around a system to create a flow of electricity.

3) The electric current is the <u>flow</u> of the electrons or ions.

Ionic Compounds Conduct Electricity when Molten or in Solution

1) Ionic compounds are made of a <u>lattice</u> of <u>positive and negative ions</u> (more on this on pages 19-22).

2) <u>Solid</u> ionic compounds <u>don't</u> conduct electricity because the ions <u>aren't</u> free to move around.

3) When an ionic compound is <u>dissolved</u> the ions separate and are <u>free to move</u> in the <u>solution</u>. This means that they'll carry <u>electric current</u> and so <u>conduct electricity</u>.

4) When an ionic compound <u>melts</u>, the ions are also <u>free to move</u> and will carry <u>electric current</u>.

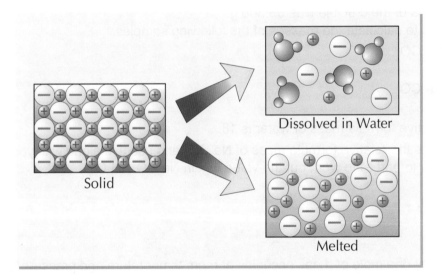

Solid

Dissolved in Water

Melted

Covalent Compounds Don't Conduct Electricity

1) Covalent compounds <u>don't contain ions</u> because they make bonds by sharing electrons (see pages 25-27).

2) This means that they don't have any charge carriers that are free to move — so they <u>can't</u> carry an <u>electric current</u>.

An important exception to this rule is graphite (page 28). Graphite has free electrons so it's a good electrical conductor.

Remember, ionic compounds can't conduct electricity when solid...

This page isn't so bad... you've just got to remember what an electrical current is and how the structure and bonding of ionic compounds and covalent compounds can explain their properties.

Electrical Conductivity

Metals are excellent electrical conductors. This page explains why.

Metals are Held Together by Metallic Bonding

1) Metals have a giant structure of positive ions surrounded by a sea of delocalised (free) electrons.

2) The attraction between the positive ions and the electrons is called metallic bonding.

3) It's this metallic bonding which gives metals their properties.

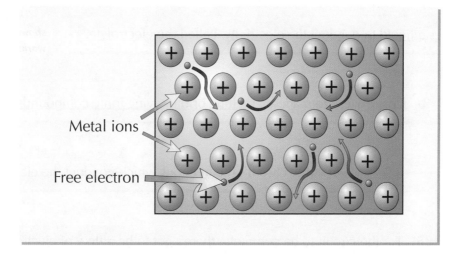

Metal ions

Free electron

Metals are Good Conductors of Electricity and Heat

The free electrons carry electrical current and heat energy through the material, so metals are good conductors of electricity and heat.

Most Metals are Malleable

The layers of atoms in a metal can slide over each other, making metals malleable — this means that they can be hammered or rolled into flat sheets.

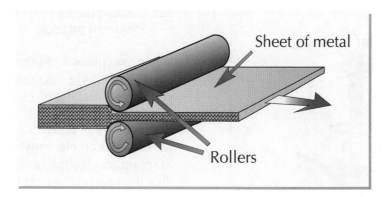

Sheet of metal

Rollers

It's all about the free electrons...

You just need to remember how the structure and bonding can explain the properties.

Electrolysis

Well, you are in for a treat. The last five pages of this section are all about <u>electrolysis</u>. Oooooooooh...

Electrolysis is Used to Make New Substances

1) If you pass an <u>electric current</u> through an <u>ionic substance</u> that's <u>molten</u> or <u>in solution</u> it breaks down into <u>new substances</u>. This is called <u>electrolysis</u>.

2) It requires a <u>liquid</u> to <u>conduct</u> the <u>electricity</u>, called the <u>electrolyte</u>.

There's a diagram showing how electrolysis works on the next page.

3) Electrolytes are made by <u>melting</u> or <u>dissolving ionic compounds</u>.

4) In either case it's the <u>free ions</u> which <u>conduct</u> the electricity.

5) For the circuit to be complete, there's got to be a <u>flow of electrons</u>. <u>Electrons</u> are taken <u>away from</u> ions at a <u>positive electrode (anode)</u> and <u>given to</u> other ions at a <u>negative electrode (cathode)</u>.

6) As ions gain or lose electrons they become <u>atoms</u> or <u>molecules</u>.

Electrolytes are Liquids that Conduct Electricity

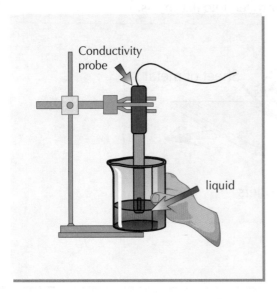

Conductivity probe

liquid

1) When you place a <u>conductivity probe</u> in an <u>electrolyte</u>, <u>current</u> flows through the circuit — so you can <u>measure</u> its <u>conductivity</u>.

2) When you place a conductivity probe in a <u>non-electrolyte</u>, <u>no current</u> flows, so you'll get a reading of <u>zero</u> conductivity.

3) Another way of determining whether a substance is an electrolyte or not is to set up an <u>electrolytic cell</u> (like the one on the next page).

4) If the substance will <u>undergo electrolysis</u> then it <u>is</u> an electrolyte.

Electrolysis of Lead Bromide

In *Molten* Ionic Compounds There's Only *One* Source of *Ions*

1) <u>Molten</u> ionic compounds can be electrolysed because the ions can <u>move freely</u>.

2) They're usually broken up into their <u>elements</u>.

3) A good example of this is the electrolysis of <u>molten lead bromide</u> ($PbBr_2$):

You can melt lead bromide using a Bunsen burner.

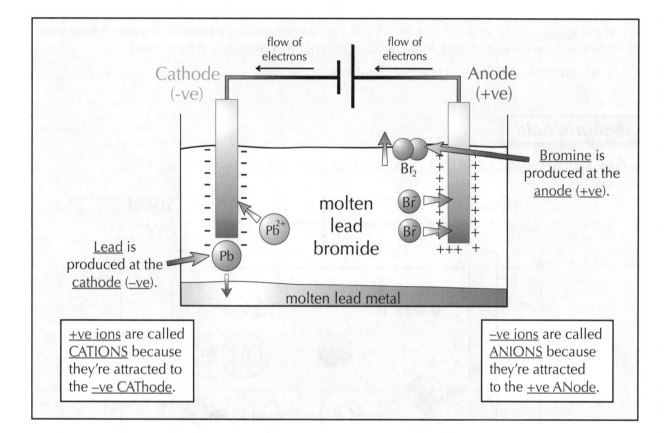

Cathode (-ve)

flow of electrons

flow of electrons

Anode (+ve)

Br_2

molten lead bromide

Pb^{2+}

Br^-

Br^-

<u>Bromine</u> is produced at the <u>anode (+ve)</u>.

<u>Lead</u> is produced at the <u>cathode (–ve)</u>.

Pb

molten lead metal

+ve ions are called CATIONS because they're attracted to the –ve CAThode.

–ve ions are called ANIONS because they're attracted to the +ve ANode.

4) You can write <u>half-equations</u> to show what's happening at each <u>electrode</u>.

5) The <u>+ve</u> Pb^{2+} ions are attracted to the <u>–ve cathode</u>. At the <u>cathode</u> a lead ion <u>accepts two electrons</u> to become a <u>lead atom</u>. The <u>molten lead</u> that forms will <u>sink</u> to the bottom.

$$Pb^{2+} + 2e^- \rightarrow Pb$$

6) The <u>–ve</u> Br^- ions are attracted to the <u>+ve anode</u>. At the <u>anode</u> two bromide ions <u>lose one electron</u> each and become a <u>bromine molecule</u>. Brown <u>bromine gas</u> forms at the <u>top</u> of the anode.

$$2Br^- \rightarrow Br_2 + 2e^-$$

7) The <u>electrodes</u> are made from an <u>inert</u> (unreactive) material so they <u>don't</u> take part in the reaction.

Learn this lead bromide example...

In the exam you could be asked to describe how molten salts can be electrolysed. If you understand how the electrolysis of lead bromide works, then you can apply your knowledge to different salts.

Electrolysis of Aqueous Solutions

Here's another lovely page all about <u>electrolysis</u>. Enjoy.

Electrolysis of Aqueous Solutions is a Bit More Complicated

1) In <u>aqueous solutions</u>, as well as the <u>ions</u> from the ionic compound,
there will be <u>hydrogen ions</u> (H^+) and <u>hydroxide ions</u> (OH^-) from the <u>water</u>.

2) At the <u>cathode</u>, if <u>H^+ ions</u> and <u>metal ions</u> are present, <u>hydrogen gas</u> will be produced if the metal
ions are <u>more reactive</u> than the H^+ ions (e.g. sodium ions). If the metal ions are <u>less reactive</u> than
the H^+ ions (e.g. copper ions), a solid layer of the <u>pure metal</u> will be produced instead.

3) At the <u>anode</u>, if <u>OH^-</u> and <u>halide ions</u> (Cl^-, Br^-, I^-) are present, molecules of chlorine, bromine or
iodine will be formed. If <u>no halide ions</u> are present, then <u>oxygen</u> will be formed.

4) Here's one example that you need to know about:

Sulfuric Acid

A solution of <u>sulfuric acid</u> (H_2SO_4) contains <u>three different ions</u>: SO_4^{2-}, H^+ and OH^-.

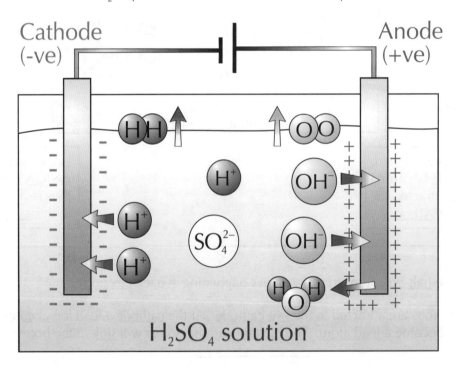

- <u>Hydrogen ions</u> (from the water or sulfuric acid) accept electrons.
So at the cathode, <u>hydrogen gas</u> is produced.
$$2H^+ + 2e^- \rightarrow H_2$$

- <u>Hydroxide ions</u> lose electrons more easily than sulfate ions.
So at the anode <u>oxygen</u> and <u>water</u> are produced.
$$4OH^- \rightarrow O_2 + 2H_2O + 4e^-$$

Acid + Electricity = Health and Safety Nightmare...

At first glance it might not be obvious what's happening in this example. But you'll be fine if you
relax, take your time with it and make sure you understand what's happening at each electrode.

Electrolysis of Aqueous Solutions

Two more examples of electrolysis of aqueous solutions, coming right up.

Sodium Chloride:

A solution of <u>sodium chloride</u> (NaCl) contains <u>four different ions</u>: Na^+, Cl^-, OH^- and H^+.

- <u>Hydrogen ions</u> accept electrons more easily than sodium ions. So at the cathode, <u>hydrogen gas</u> is produced.

$$2H^+ + 2e^- \rightarrow H_2$$

- <u>Chloride ions</u> lose electrons more easily than hydroxide ions. So at the anode <u>chlorine gas</u> is produced.

$$2Cl^- \rightarrow Cl_2 + 2e^-$$

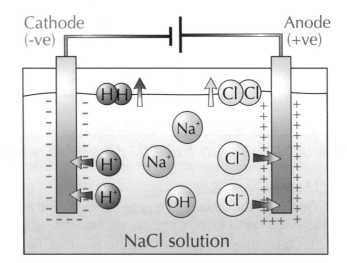

NaCl solution

Copper(II) Sulfate:

A solution of <u>copper(II) sulfate</u> (CuSO$_4$) contains <u>four different ions</u>: Cu^{2+}, SO_4^{2-}, H^+ and OH^-.

- <u>Copper ions</u> accept electrons more easily than hydrogen ions. So at the cathode, <u>copper metal</u> is produced.

$$Cu^{2+} + 2e^- \rightarrow Cu$$

- <u>Hydroxide ions</u> lose electrons more easily than sulfate ions. So at the anode <u>oxygen</u> and <u>water</u> are produced.

$$4OH^- \rightarrow O_2 + 2H_2O + 4e^-$$

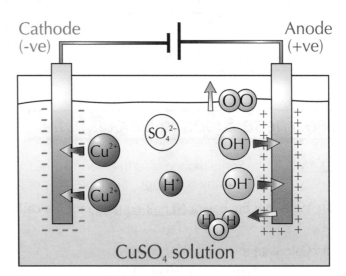

CuSO$_4$ solution

If only revision was made up of positive ions...

Then we could reduce it using electrolysis. You need to make sure that you can remember the half-equations for the electrolytes at both electrodes... Phew. I think I need to lie down...

Electrolysis — Calculating Masses

Will the electrolysis never end... (Well, yes — this is the end of the section, huzzah.)

No. of Electrons Transferred *Increases* with *Time* and *Current*

1) The amount of product made by electrolysis depends on the number of electrons that are transferred.

2) If you increase the number of electrons, you increase the amount of substance produced.

> This can be achieved by:
> - electrolysing for a longer time.
> - increasing the current.

Coulombs and Faradays are Amounts of Electricity

1) One amp flowing for one second means a charge of one coulomb has moved.

2) Generally, the amount of charge (Q, measured in coulombs) flowing through a circuit is equal to the current (I) measured in amps multiplied by the time in seconds (t):

$$Q = I\,t$$

3) 96 000 coulombs (amps × seconds) is called one faraday.

4) One faraday (F) contains one mole of electrons.

One Mole of Product Needs 'n' Moles of Electrons

A sodium ion needs one electron to make a sodium atom. So one mole of sodium ions is going to need one mole of electrons (one faraday) to make one mole of sodium atoms. But an ion with a 2^+ charge needs two moles of electrons to make one mole of atoms, and, guess what, three for a 3^+ charge...

$Na^+ + e^- \rightarrow Na$	1 mole of sodium ions + 1 mole of electrons → 1 mole of sodium atoms
$Zn^{2+} + 2e^- \rightarrow Zn$	1 mole of zinc ions + 2 moles of electrons → 1 mole of zinc atoms
$Al^{3+} + 3e^- \rightarrow Al$	1 mole of aluminium ions + 3 moles of electrons → 1 mole of aluminium atoms

Use These Steps in Calculations

EXAMPLE: Some molten lead(II) chloride ($PbCl_2$) is electrolysed for 20 minutes. The current flowing is 5 amps. Find the mass of lead produced.

1) Write out the balanced half-equation for the cathode.

$$Pb^{2+} + 2e^- \rightarrow Pb$$

Writing the half-equation is easier if you remember that the full equation is: $PbCl_2 \rightarrow Pb + Cl_2$

2) Calculate the number of faradays.

Charge (coulombs) = current (amps) × time (s) = 5 × (20 × 60) = 6000 coulombs.

Number of faradays = 6000 / 96 000 = 0.0625 F

3) Calculate the number of moles of lead produced.

(divide the number of faradays by the number of electrons in the half-equation)

0.0625 ÷ 2 = 0.03125 moles of lead atoms.

4) Write in the M_r values from the periodic table to work out the mass of solid lead produced.

Mass of lead = M_r × No. of moles = 207 × 0.03125 = 6.5 g (to 1 d.p.)

Warm-Up and Exam Questions

I bet you think you know everything there is to know about electrolysis after that section. Well, here's your chance to prove it. Get started with the warm-up questions, then it's exam practice time.

Warm-Up Questions

1) Name the process in which an electric current is passed through an ionic compound to make a new substance.

2) What state must an ionic compound be in if it's to be used as an electrolyte?

3) Which electrode are positive ions attracted to during electrolysis?

Exam Questions

1   An experiment was carried out to find out if the ionic compound magnesium oxide conducts electricity. The compound was tested when it was solid, dissolved in water and molten.

a)   Copy and complete the table of results.

State	Conducts electricity? (yes/no)
Solid	
Dissolved in water	
Molten	

(3 marks)

b)   Explain your answers to part a).

(2 marks)

c)   To conduct electricity a compound must be able to carry an electric current. Explain what is meant by the term electric current.

(1 mark)

d)   Explain why most covalent compounds don't conduct electricity.

(2 marks)

2   Metals are held together by metallic bonding.

a)   Metallic bonding occurs due to the structure of a metal. Describe the structure of a metal.

(1 mark)

b)   Metals are good conductors of electricity and most are malleable. Explain why metals have these properties by referring to metallic structures and bonding.

(2 marks)

PAPER 2

3   Electrolysis using inert electrodes can be carried out with several different aqueous solutions.

a)   An aqueous solution of sodium chloride ($NaCl$) is being electrolysed.

i)   Predict the product formed at the negative electrode in this reaction and give its state.

(2 marks)

ii)   Predict the product formed at the positive electrode in this reaction and give its state.

(2 marks)

b)   Explain why the product at the negative electrode is formed.

(1 mark)

Exam Questions

4 The diagram below shows the electrolysis of lead bromide.

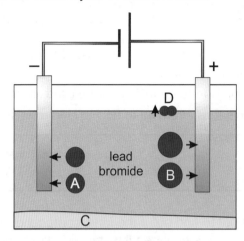

a) Choose from the letters **A**, **B**, **C** or **D** to identify the
   following substances on the diagram.

   Pb^{2+} molten lead Br^- Br_2

   (2 marks)

b) Write a balanced half-equation for the process that occurs
   at the negative electrode during the electrolysis of lead bromide.

   (2 marks)

c) Write a balanced half-equation for the process that occurs
   at the positive electrode during the electrolysis of lead bromide.

   (2 marks)

d) In electrolysis, a liquid ionic substance such as lead bromide is needed to
   conduct electricity and allow current to flow around the electrolytic cell.

   i)   State the name given to these conductive substances.

        (1 mark)

   ii) Describe an experiment to test whether a particular substance
        can be used for this purpose.

        (2 marks)

   iii) Lead bromide is an ionic substance which doesn't easily dissolve in water.
        How could it be made into a liquid for electrolysis?

        (1 mark)

PAPER 2

5 Molten silver nitrate was electrolysed for 40 minutes using a current of 0.2 amps.
  The half-equation for the reaction is:

$$Ag^+ + e^- \rightarrow Ag$$

a) Calculate the number of faradays that flowed during the electrolysis.
   Take the value of 1 faraday to be 96 000 coulombs.

   (2 marks)

b) How many moles of silver were deposited at the negative electrode?

   (1 mark)

c) Calculate the mass of silver deposited at the negative electrode.

   (2 marks)

Revision Summary for Section 1 — 2

Right. Here you go. One list of very important questions to test whether you've learnt this section properly. There's no backing out now — make sure you can answer each and every one of these questions, without any sneaky peeks. If you're struggling, go back through the section, have a browse and then try again. Repeat this until you can do them all perfectly. Have fun.

1) What do the following state symbols stand for?
   a) (l)   b) (aq)   c) (g)

2)* Balance these symbol equations:
   a) $Na + H_2O \rightarrow NaOH + H_2$ b) $Al + HCl \rightarrow AlCl_3 + H_2$

3)* The table below gives the masses and relative abundances of the isotopes of neon:

relative mass of isotope	relative abundance
20	91%
22	9%

   Calculate the relative atomic mass of neon. Give your answer to 2 decimal places.

4)* Find the relative formula mass of the following compounds.   *Hint: there's a Periodic table on the*
   a) H_2SO_4 b) $ZnCO_3$ c) CH_3COONa d) $C(CH_3)_4$ *inside of the front cover.*

5)* Using the periodic table, find the empirical formula of the compound formed when 227 g of calcium reacts with 216 g of fluorine.

6)* A molecule has an empirical formula of C_2H_5Cl, and a relative molecular mass of 258. Work out its molecular formula.

7)* a) What mass of sodium oxide (Na_2O) is produced when 50 g of sodium is burnt in air?

   b) Briony does this reaction and ends up with 42.3 g of sodium oxide. What is the percentage yield of her reaction?

8)* How many moles are there in 147 g of sodium hydroxide (NaOH)?

9)* What is the mass of 0.05 moles of magnesium oxide (MgO)?

10)* Heating hydrated iron chloride, $FeCl_2.XH_2O$, in a crucible forms anhydrous iron chloride, $FeCl_2$. Using the experimental data below, find the value of X and write the formula of the hydrated salt.

Mass of empty crucible	23.299 g
Mass of crucible + mass $FeCl_2.XH_2O$	28.133 g
Mass of crucible + $FeCl_2$	26.347 g

11)* What's the volume of 3.7 moles of nitrogen at RTP?

12)* How many moles of sodium hydroxide are in 250 cm³ of a 2 mol/dm³ solution of NaOH?

13)* 0.55 moles of sodium sulfate are dissolved in 500 cm³ of water. What is the concentration in mol/dm³ of the solution made?

14) When are ionic compounds able to conduct electricity?

15) Why are metals good conductors of heat and electricity?

16) Draw and label a diagram to show the electrolysis of lead(II) bromide.

17) Write the half-equations for the electrolysis of copper(II) sulfate, $CuSO_4$.

18)* Find the mass of lead liberated if 3 amps flows for 40 minutes during the electrolysis of lead(II) bromide ($PbBr_2$).

*Answers on pages 191-192.

More About the Periodic Table

Remember that big ol' periodic table back on page 16. Well there's more about it on this page and the next. It has all the elements in a nice logical order, which makes it great for spotting trends. Honest.

The *Periodic Table* is Arranged in *Periods*...

1) The rows of the periodic table are called periods.

2) The properties of elements change as you go along a period (sometimes quite dramatically).

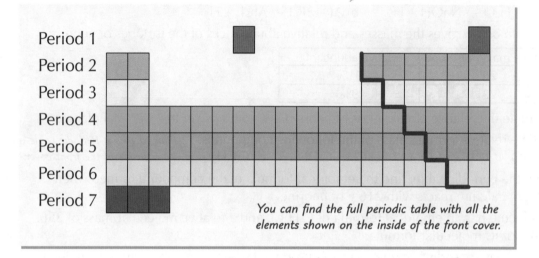

You can find the full periodic table with all the elements shown on the inside of the front cover.

...and *Groups*

1) The columns of the periodic table are called groups.

2) Elements in the same group have similar chemical properties.

   LEARN THIS: This is because they have the same number of electrons in their outer shell.

3) The properties of elements (such as reactivity) often gradually change as you go down a group (i.e. as the atomic number increases).

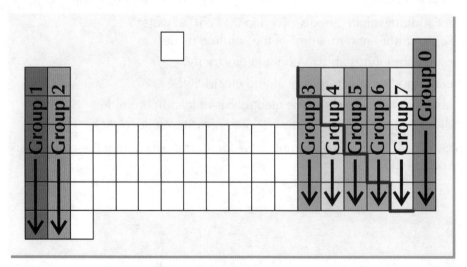

More About the Periodic Table

The Elements can be Classified as **Metals** or **Non-Metals**

The periodic table can be <u>split</u> into two parts — the <u>metals</u> are on one side and the <u>non-metals</u> are on the other.

Metals

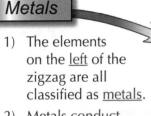

1) The elements on the <u>left</u> of the zigzag are all classified as <u>metals</u>.

2) Metals <u>conduct electricity</u> because they allow charge to pass through them easily.

3) <u>Metal oxides</u> are <u>basic</u>. This means they will neutralise acids. Metal oxides which dissolve will form solutions with a <u>pH</u> of <u>more than 7</u>.

Non-metals

1) The elements on the <u>right</u> of the zigzag are all classified as <u>non-metals</u>.

2) Non-metals are <u>poor conductors</u> of <u>electricity</u>.

3) <u>Non-metal oxides</u> are <u>acidic</u>. They dissolve in water to form solutions with a <u>pH</u> of <u>less than 7</u>.

Group 0 Elements are All **Inert**, Colourless Gases

Group 6	Group 7	Group 0
		4 **He** Helium 2
O	F	20 **Ne** Neon 10
S	Cl	40 **Ar** Argon 18
Se	Br	84 **Kr** Krypton 36
Te	I	131 **Xe** Xenon 54
Po	At	222 **Rn** Radon 86

1) Group 0 elements are called the <u>noble gases</u> and include the elements <u>helium</u>, <u>neon</u> and <u>argon</u> (plus a few others).

2) They are <u>inert</u> — this means they <u>don't react</u> with much at all.

3) The reason for this is that they have a <u>full outer shell</u> of electrons. This means they're <u>not</u> desperate to <u>give up</u> or <u>gain</u> electrons.

There are more metals than non-metals

The stuff on this page and the previous one is all really straightforward. But it's all essential Chemistry knowledge and it could easily come up in the exam. So make sure you learn it.

Group 1 — The Alkali Metals

Alkali metals all have <u>one electron</u> in their outermost shell, which makes them very <u>reactive</u>.

Group 1 Elements All *React* in a *Similar Way* with *Water*

1) <u>Simple reactions</u> can be used to work out if an element is part of the same <u>family</u> as other elements. Elements of the same family will react in a similar way.

2) For example, when <u>lithium</u>, <u>sodium</u> and <u>potassium</u> are put in <u>water</u>, they all react <u>vigorously</u>.

3) The <u>reaction</u> produces a <u>metal hydroxide</u> solution. This solution is <u>alkaline</u> — this is why Group 1 elements are known as the <u>alkali metals</u>.

4) The <u>reaction</u> of the alkali metals with water also produces <u>hydrogen</u> — this is why you can see <u>fizzing</u>. These reactions can be written as <u>chemical equations</u> — e.g. for <u>sodium</u> the equation is...

> Word equation: **sodium + water → sodium hydroxide + hydrogen**
>
> Symbol equation: $2Na_{(s)} + 2H_2O_{(l)} \rightarrow 2NaOH_{(aq)} + H_{2(g)}$

<u>*STATE SYMBOLS*</u>: *(s) = <u>solid</u>, (l) = <u>liquid</u>, (aq) = <u>aqueous</u> (dissolved in water), (g) = <u>gas</u>*

Group 1 Elements Become *More Reactive* Down the Group

1) As you go <u>down</u> Group 1 the elements become <u>more reactive</u>.

2) You can see this in the <u>rate of reaction</u> with water (i.e. the time taken for a lump of the same size of each element to <u>react completely</u> with the water and disappear).

3) <u>Lithium</u> takes longer than sodium or potassium to react, so it's the <u>least reactive</u>.

4) <u>Potassium</u> takes the shortest time to react of these three elements, so it's the <u>most reactive</u>.

> **The elements in <u>GROUP 1</u> get <u>MORE REACTIVE</u> as the <u>ATOMIC NUMBER INCREASES</u>.**

<u>REACTIONS WITH WATER</u>

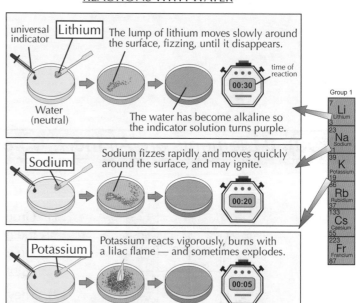

Atoms *Lose* Electrons *More Easily Down* the Group

1) All <u>Group 1</u> metals have <u>1 electron</u> in their outer shell.

2) As you go <u>down</u> Group 1, the <u>outermost electron</u> is in a shell that's <u>further from the nucleus</u>.

3) Which means the <u>attraction</u> between the <u>outermost electron</u> and the <u>nucleus</u> becomes <u>less</u>.

4) So as you go down Group 1 the atoms get <u>bigger</u>, the outer electron is <u>more easily lost</u>, and the metals are <u>more reactive</u>.

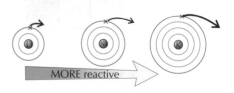

MORE reactive

Paper 2

Paper 2

Group 7 — The Halogens

The halogens are all <u>one electron short</u> of having a full outer shell.

HALOGEN — Seven Letters — Group 7

1) The elements in <u>Group 7</u> of the periodic table are called the <u>halogens</u>.

2) The <u>properties</u> of the elements in <u>Group 7</u> change <u>gradually</u> as you go <u>down</u> the group (i.e. as the atomic number <u>increases</u>). Look at the table below.

		Properties		
Group VII Elements	Atomic number	Colour	Physical state at room temperature	Boiling point
Chlorine	17	green	gas	–34 °C
Bromine	35	red-brown	liquid	59 °C
Iodine	53	dark grey	solid	185 °C

	Group 0
	He

Group 5	Group 6	Group 7	
	O	19 F Fluorine 9	Ne
	S	35.5 Cl Chlorine 17	Ar
	Se	80 Br Bromine 35	Kr
	Te	127 I Iodine 53	Xe
	Po	210 At Astatine 85	Rn

3) As the <u>atomic number</u> of the halogens <u>increases</u>, the elements have a <u>darker colour</u> and a <u>higher boiling point</u> (which is why they go from <u>gases</u> at the top of Group 7 to <u>solids</u> at the bottom, at room temperature).

4) The <u>higher up</u> Group 7 an element is, the <u>more reactive</u> it is. This is because the shell with the missing electron is <u>nearer to the nucleus</u>, so the pull from the <u>positive nucleus</u> is <u>greater</u>.

5) You might need to use these trends to <u>predict</u> the properties of <u>other halogens</u>, e.g. fluorine.

Hydrogen Chloride Gas Dissociates in Water...

1) Halogens can combine with hydrogen to form <u>hydrogen halides</u>, for example, <u>hydrogen chloride</u> and <u>hydrogen bromide</u>.

2) <u>Hydrogen chloride</u> has the chemical formula <u>HCl</u> and is a <u>gas</u> at room temperature.

3) When hydrogen chloride is dissolved in water the HCl molecules <u>split up</u> into <u>H^+ ions</u> and <u>Cl^- ions</u> — this process is called <u>dissociation</u>.

4) The solution that is formed is called <u>hydrochloric acid</u>.

5) Hydrochloric acid is an <u>acidic solution</u> (obviously) because it contains H^+ ions.

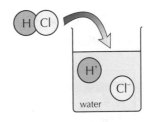

The HCl dissociates and produces H^+ ions in water, so it's acidic.

If you test a solution of hydrochloric acid with <u>blue litmus paper</u> the paper will turn <u>red/pink</u>.

...but Not in Methylbenzene

1) If HCl is dissolved in an organic solvent like <u>methylbenzene</u>, it <u>doesn't dissociate</u> into H^+ ions and Cl^- ions.

2) This means there are <u>no H^+ ions</u> produced so it's <u>not acidic</u>.

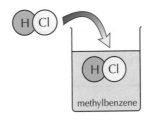

The HCl doesn't dissociate to produce H^+ ions in methylbenzene, so it's not acidic.

If you test a solution of HCl in methylbenzene with <u>blue litmus paper</u> the paper will <u>stay blue</u>. But if there is <u>any moisture</u> on the paper or in the bottle then the HCl <u>can dissociate</u> and it will behave like an <u>acid</u> again.

Displacement Reactions

The halogens are a competitive lot. The <u>more reactive</u> ones will <u>push</u> the others out of a compound.

More Reactive Halogens will Displace Less Reactive Ones

1) The elements in Group 7 take part in <u>displacement reactions</u>.

2) A <u>displacement reaction</u> is where a <u>more reactive</u> element "<u>pushes out</u>" (displaces) a <u>less reactive</u> element from a compound.

3) For example, <u>chlorine</u> is more reactive than <u>iodine</u> (it's higher up Group 7).

4) So, if you add <u>chlorine water</u> to <u>potassium iodide</u> solution the chlorine will react with the potassium in the potassium iodide to form <u>potassium chloride</u>.

5) The <u>iodine</u> is <u>displaced from the salt</u> and gets left in the solution, turning it <u>brown</u>.

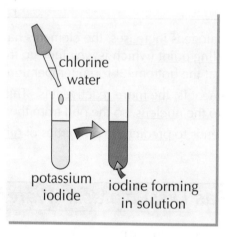

6) The table below shows what happens when you mix different combinations of <u>chlorine</u>, <u>bromine</u> and <u>iodine</u> with the salts <u>potassium chloride</u>, <u>potassium bromide</u> and <u>potassium iodide</u>.

	Potassium chloride solution KCl(aq) — colourless	Potassium bromide solution KBr(aq) — colourless	Potassium iodide solution KI(aq) — colourless
Chlorine water Cl_2(aq) — colourless	no reaction	orange solution (Br_2) formed	brown solution (I_2) formed
Bromine water Br_2(aq) — orange	no reaction	no reaction	brown solution (I_2) formed
Iodine water I_2(aq) — brown	no reaction	no reaction	no reaction

These experiments are dead easy. All you need to do is add a <u>few drops</u> of the <u>halogen solution</u> to the <u>salt solution</u>. Then look for a <u>colour change</u>.

Displacement Reactions

This is where displacement reactions get slightly trickier I'm afraid.
You need to know what the <u>electrons</u> are doing.

Halogen Displacement Reactions Involve *Transfer of Electrons*

1) You can show the <u>displacement reactions</u> between halogens and salt solutions as <u>equations</u>. E.g.

$$Cl_2(aq) + 2KI(aq) \rightarrow I_2(aq) + 2KCl(aq)$$

This is the equation for chlorine displacing iodine from potassium iodide. They might give you a different example in the exam, but the principle is always the same.

2) When this reaction happens <u>electrons</u> are <u>passed</u> from the iodine to the chlorine.

> Each chlorine atom in the Cl_2 molecule gains an electron to form two negative Cl^- ions.
>
> $$Cl_2(aq) + 2I^-(aq) \rightarrow 2Cl^-(aq) + I_2(aq)$$
>
> Two iodide ions lose an electron each and then form a neutral I_2 molecule.

3) A <u>loss of electrons</u> is called <u>oxidation</u>. A <u>gain in electrons</u> is called <u>reduction</u>.

4) In displacement reactions, reduction and oxidation happen <u>simultaneously</u> —
   for example, in this reaction the <u>chlorine is reduced</u> and the <u>iodine is oxidised</u>.

5) An <u>oxidising agent</u> accepts electrons and <u>gets reduced</u>. So, here <u>chlorine</u> is an oxidising agent.

6) A <u>reducing agent</u> donates electrons and <u>gets oxidised</u>. So <u>iodine</u> is a reducing agent.

7) Reactions where reduction and oxidation happen at the same time are called <u>redox reactions</u>.

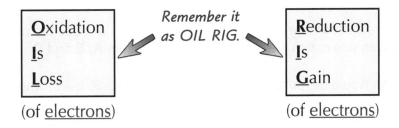

Oxidation	*Remember it*	**R**eduction
Is	*as OIL RIG.*	**I**s
Loss		**G**ain
(of <u>electrons</u>)		(of <u>electrons</u>)

Remember, displacement reactions are a type of redox reaction

Redox reactions are definitely tricky to get your head around and the best way to get through it is to remember OIL RIG — <u>Oxidation Is Loss</u>, <u>Reduction Is Gain</u> (of electrons). This handy little memory aid will definitely help you out with all types of tricky redox questions. Promise.

Warm-Up and Exam Questions

OK. Here are a few questions to have a go at. Don't panic — as long as you've learnt everything on the previous few pages you'll be absolutely fine.

Warm-Up Questions

1) A solution of an oxide has a pH higher than 7. Is it a metal or a non-metal oxide? Explain your answer.

2) Explain why sodium and potassium undergo similar reactions with water.

3) Explain why Group 0 elements are unreactive.

4) What is oxidation? What is reduction?

Exam Questions

1 The diagram shows the position of the element bismuth in the periodic table.

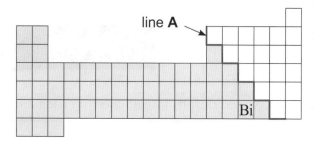

a) What is the name for a row of elements in the periodic table?

(1 mark)

Element **X** is found in the same group of the periodic table as bismuth.

b) What does that tell you about the two elements' properties?

(1 mark)

c) Element **X** does not conduct electricity. Predict whether element **X** will be found to the left or the right of line **A** in the diagram above. Explain your answer.

(2 marks)

2 A teacher dropped small, similar sized pieces of three different alkali metals, **A**, **B** and **C**, into water. The students recorded the time taken for each piece to react completely.

Metal	Time taken to react (s)
A	27
B	8
C	42

a) State which of these metals, **A**, **B** or **C**, is the most reactive. Explain how you know.

(2 marks)

b) The three metals used were lithium, sodium and potassium. Use the results shown in the table to match them up to the correct letters **A**, **B** and **C**.

(2 marks)

c) What products would be formed in a reaction between sodium and water?

(2 marks)

d) One of the students said, "The amount of time taken for rubidium to react with water would be shorter than for metal **A**, but longer than for metal **B**". Why is the student incorrect?

(2 marks)

PAPER 2

e) Explain why alkali metals become more reactive as their atomic number increases.

(3 marks)

Exam Questions

3   The properties of the elements within Group 7 change as you go down the group.

a)   Look at the table below. State the **two** missing pieces of information.

Element	Atomic number	Colour	Boiling point (°C)	Physical state at 25 °C
chlorine	17		−34	gas
bromine	35	red-brown	59	liquid
iodine	53	dark grey	185	

(2 marks)

b)   Fluorine is another Group 7 element.

i)   How would you expect the reactivity of fluorine to
compare to the reactivity of chlorine?

(1 mark)

ii)   Predict the physical state of fluorine at 25 °C.

(1 mark)

4   Chlorine gas and hydrogen gas can react together to make hydrogen chloride.

a)   Write a balanced chemical equation for this reaction. Include state symbols.

(3 marks)

b)   Some of the product of this reaction is dissolved in water.
The rest of the product is dissolved in methylbenzene (an organic solvent).

i)   Explain, in terms of dissociation, the difference
in the **acidity** of these two solutions.

(4 marks)

ii)   Name the solution formed when hydrogen chloride gas dissolves in water.

(1 mark)

5   Halogens can take part in displacement reactions with halogen salts.

a)   State what is meant by the term **displacement reaction**.

(1 mark)

b)   When bromine water is added to potassium iodide solution a reaction will take place.

i)   Write a symbol equation for the reaction.

(2 marks)

ii)   Explain why this reaction happens.

(2 marks)

c)   The reaction of bromine water with potassium iodide solution is a redox reaction.

i)   State what is meant by the term **redox reaction**.

(1 mark)

ii)   Identify the substance which acts as an oxidising agent
when bromine water is added to potassium iodide.

(1 mark)

6   When chlorine water is added to a solution of potassium bromide, a chemical reaction occurs.
State the colour of the solution before and after the reaction.

(2 marks)

Reactions of Metals

You can use the reactions of different metals with <u>dilute acids</u> to work out how <u>reactive</u> they are.

Acid + Metal → Salt + Hydrogen

Here's the **Typical Experiment**:

1) The more <u>reactive</u> the metal, the <u>faster</u> the reaction will go —
   very reactive metals (e.g. sodium) react <u>explosively</u>.

2) The <u>speed</u> of reaction is indicated by the <u>rate</u> at which the <u>bubbles</u> of hydrogen are given off.

3) The <u>hydrogen</u> is confirmed by the <u>burning splint test</u> (see page 81).

Here are some examples:

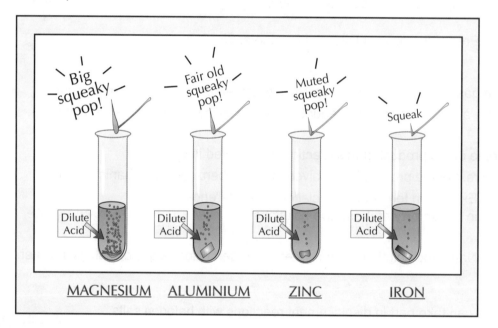

Magnesium

Magnesium reacts <u>vigorously</u> with <u>cold</u> dilute acids and produces <u>loads of bubbles</u>.

Aluminium

Aluminium doesn't react much with cold dilute acids because it has a protective aluminium oxide layer. But, it reacts <u>vigorously</u> with <u>warm</u> dilute acids and produces <u>a lot</u> of bubbles.

Zinc and Iron

Both zinc and iron react <u>slowly</u> with dilute acids but more strongly if you heat them up.

Reactions of Metals

As you saw on the previous page, metals react with dilute acids to produce a salt and hydrogen.

The **Name** of the **Salt** Depends on the **Metal** and **Acid** Used

1) Metals <u>react</u> with dilute <u>hydrochloric acid</u> and <u>sulfuric acid</u> in the <u>same way</u>, but <u>different salts</u> are formed depending on the acid used.

2) <u>Hydrochloric acid</u> will always produce <u>chloride salts</u>.

   For example: hydrochloric acid + magnesium → magnesium chloride + hydrogen

   hydrochloric acid + aluminium → aluminium chloride + hydrogen

3) <u>Sulfuric acid</u> will always produce <u>sulfate salts</u>.

   For example: sulfuric acid + magnesium → magnesium sulfate + hydrogen

   sulfuric acid + potassium → potassium sulfate + hydrogen

Metals Also React with **Water**

The <u>reactions</u> of metals with <u>water</u> also show the reactivity of metals.

Metal + Water → Metal Hydroxide + Hydrogen
(Less reactive Metal + Steam → Metal oxide + Hydrogen)

1) Very reactive metals like <u>potassium</u>, <u>sodium</u>, <u>lithium</u> and <u>calcium</u> will all react <u>vigorously</u> with water.

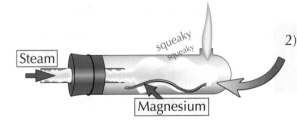

2) Less reactive metals like <u>magnesium</u>, <u>zinc</u> and <u>iron</u> won't react much with cold water but they will react with <u>steam</u>.

3) <u>Copper</u> won't react with either water or steam.

Hydrochloric acid produces chloride salts...

There's enough on these two pages to make the revision juices bubble more than a lump of potassium in a tube of dilute acid. If you react metals with water or dilute acid you'll get this order of reactivity from <u>most reactive</u> to <u>least reactive</u>: <u>Potassium</u>, <u>Sodium</u>, <u>Lithium</u>, <u>Calcium</u>, <u>Magnesium</u>, <u>Zinc</u>, <u>Iron</u>, <u>Copper</u>.

The Reactivity Series

The previous pages covered some reactions that help you work out how <u>reactive</u> a <u>metal</u> is. You can use this info to put the metals in order of their <u>reactivity</u>. Which is more useful than it sounds.

The **Reactivity Series** — How **Well** a Metal **Reacts**

The <u>reactivity series</u> lists metals in <u>order</u> of their <u>reactivity</u> towards other substances.

Make sure you learn this list:

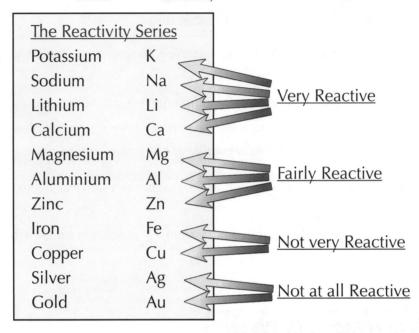

The Reactivity Series

Potassium	K
Sodium	Na
Lithium	Li
Calcium	Ca
Magnesium	Mg
Aluminium	Al
Zinc	Zn
Iron	Fe
Copper	Cu
Silver	Ag
Gold	Au

<u>Very Reactive</u>

<u>Fairly Reactive</u>

<u>Not very Reactive</u>

<u>Not at all Reactive</u>

A **More Reactive** Metal **Displaces** a **Less Reactive** Metal

1) <u>More reactive</u> metals react <u>more strongly</u> than <u>less reactive</u> metals.

2) This means that a more reactive metal will <u>displace</u> a less reactive metal from its oxide because it will bond <u>more strongly</u> to the oxygen.

   <u>Example:</u> <u>iron</u> would be displaced from <u>iron oxide</u> by the more reactive <u>aluminium</u>.

   iron oxide + aluminium   → aluminium oxide + iron

   Fe_2O_3 + $2Al$ → Al_2O_3 + $2Fe$

3) <u>Metal compounds</u> like copper sulfate, zinc chloride and sodium chloride are <u>metal salts</u>.

4) If you put a <u>reactive metal</u> into a solution of a <u>less reactive metal salt</u> the reactive metal will <u>replace</u> the <u>less reactive metal</u> in the salt.

   <u>Example:</u> put an <u>iron nail</u> in a solution of <u>copper sulfate</u> and the more reactive iron will "<u>kick out</u>" the less reactive copper from the salt. You end up with <u>iron sulfate solution</u> and <u>copper metal</u>.

   copper sulfate + iron   → iron sulfate + copper

   $CuSO_4$ + Fe → $FeSO_4$ + Cu

5) If a piece of <u>silver metal</u> is put into a solution of copper sulfate, <u>nothing happens</u>. The more reactive metal (copper) is <u>already</u> in the salt.

6) You can use displacement reactions to <u>work out</u> where in the reactivity series a metal is supposed to go. For example, if you were given a lump of a mystery metal, you could try reacting it with different <u>metal oxides</u> and <u>salts</u>. If it <u>reacted</u> with copper oxide you'd know it was <u>higher</u> in the series than copper. If it <u>didn't react</u> with magnesium sulfate you'd know it was lower than magnesium in the reactivity series.

Iron

Iron's <u>strength</u> has made it a very important metal that's used throughout the world for <u>building construction</u>, <u>car manufacture</u> and wrought iron <u>garden furniture</u>. But the problem is — it rusts...

Iron and Steel **Corrode** to Make **Rust**

The word "rust" is only used for the corrosion of iron, not other metals.

1) Iron corrodes easily. In other words, it <u>rusts</u>.

2) Rusting only happens when the iron's in contact with both <u>oxygen</u> (from the air) and <u>water</u>.

3) The chemical reaction that takes place when iron corrodes is an <u>oxidation</u> reaction. The iron <u>gains oxygen</u> to form <u>iron(III) oxide</u>.

4) Water then becomes loosely bonded to the iron(III) oxide and the result is <u>hydrated iron(III) oxide</u> — which we call rust.

5) Learn the <u>word equation</u> for the reaction:

$$\text{iron + oxygen + water} \rightarrow \text{hydrated iron(III) oxide (rust)}$$

6) Unfortunately, rust is a soft crumbly solid that soon <u>flakes off</u> to leave more iron available to <u>rust again</u>.

There are **Two** Main Ways to **Prevent Rusting**

1) The obvious way to prevent rusting is to <u>coat the iron</u> with a <u>barrier</u> to keep out the water and oxygen.

<u>BARRIER METHODS</u>:

> <u>Painting/Coating with plastic</u> — ideal for big and small structures alike. Can be decorative too.

> <u>Oiling/Greasing</u> — this has to be used when moving parts are involved, like on bike chains.

2) The other way is the <u>sacrificial method</u>. This involves placing a <u>more reactive metal</u> with the iron. The water and oxygen then react with this sacrificial metal <u>instead</u> of with the iron.

- <u>Zinc</u> is often used as a sacrificial metal.
- The zinc is <u>more reactive</u> than iron — it's further up the reactivity series.
- So, the zinc will be oxidised <u>instead</u> of the iron.
- A <u>coating of zinc</u> can be sprayed onto the object — this is known as <u>galvanising</u>.
- Or big <u>blocks of zinc</u> can be bolted to the iron. This is used on ships' hulls, or on underground iron pipes.

Rust = hydrated iron(III) oxide

So there you have it folks. Make sure you learn all the stuff on this page by <u>covering</u> the page and <u>writing it all out again</u> — not that you need me to remind you of the method of course...

Warm-Up and Exam Questions

Some more questions for you. You know what to do by now. Get cracking...

1) Magnesium is reacted with dilute hydrochloric acid. Give the name of the salt formed.
2) Which of the following metals will react most vigorously with water?
   magnesium,   zinc,   calcium,   copper
3) Explain why a more reactive metal will displace a less reactive metal from its oxide.
4) What two things are needed for iron to rust?

Exam Questions

1   Four different metals are reacted with dilute sulfuric acid.
    The diagram below shows the reactions after 30 seconds.

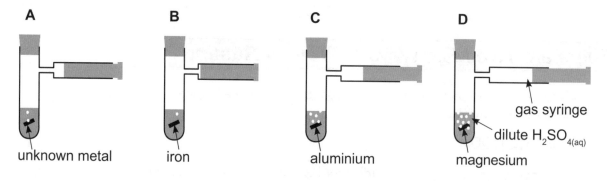

A — unknown metal
B — iron
C — aluminium
D — magnesium, gas syringe, dilute $H_2SO_{4(aq)}$

a)   Write the letters **A-D** to arrange the reactions from least
     vigorous to most vigorous going left to right.

(2 marks)

b)   Use your knowledge of the reactivity series and your answer to part a)
     to suggest which metal is the unknown metal in the diagram above.

(1 mark)

2   A student placed pieces of copper, zinc and an unknown metal in zinc sulfate solution and
    copper sulfate solution and left them for an hour. The student's results are shown below.

	zinc	copper	unidentified metal
reaction with zinc sulfate	no reaction	no reaction	no reaction
reaction with copper sulfate	reaction	no reaction	reaction

a)   Suggest the name of the unidentified metal.

(1 mark)

b)   Explain how you can tell that the unidentified metal is more reactive than copper.

(1 mark)

Exam Questions

3   In an experiment to investigate rusting, three iron nails were placed into separate test tubes.

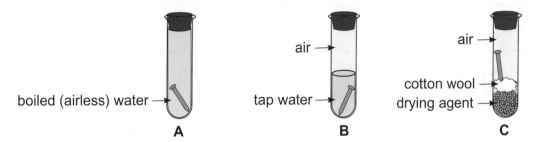

   a)   In which tube, **A**, **B** or **C**, will the nail rust?

(1 mark)

   b)   Rusting is an oxidation reaction. State what is meant by the term **oxidation**.

(1 mark)

   c)   Experiment B was repeated, but using a nail that had first been coated in paint.
        Suggest what you would observe in this experiment and explain your prediction.

(2 marks)

   d)   One method of protecting iron nails from rusting is coating with zinc.

        i)   What is the name for this method of protection?

(1 mark)

        ii) Explain how this method prevents iron from rusting even if the coating is
             scratched to reveal the iron underneath.

(2 marks)

   e)   Which of the following is the best method of preventing moving parts from rusting?
        Plastic coating   Sacrificial magnesium blocks   Oiling   Painting

(1 mark)

4   A student performed an investigation to observe the chemical reactions of four metals
     with some metal oxides. The student's results are displayed in the table below.
     The student put a tick if a reaction occurred and a cross if there was no reaction.

	aluminium oxide	copper oxide	iron oxide	magnesium oxide
aluminium	✓	✓	✓	✗
copper	✗	✗	✗	✗
iron	✗	✓	✗	✗
magnesium	✓	✓	✗	✗

   a)   Which **two** results in the table are wrong?

(2 marks)

   b)   State how many of the oxides in the table you would expect to react with gold.

(1 mark)

   c)   Which metal in the table would you expect to react most vigorously
        with copper oxide? Give a reason for your answer.

(2 marks)

Oxygen in the Atmosphere

This page is all about <u>oxygen</u> — what a breath of fresh air...

The **Atmosphere** is Mostly **Nitrogen** and **Oxygen**

For 200 million years or so, the atmosphere has been about how it is now:

78% NITROGEN

nearly 1% ARGON

21% OXYGEN

only 0.04% CO_2

There can be a lot of water vapour too.

Make sure you know the <u>proportions</u> of each gas.

You Can Use **Copper** to **Investigate** the **Proportion** of **Oxygen** in the **Atmosphere**

Here's an experiment involving <u>copper</u> that shows that the atmosphere today contains around <u>one fifth oxygen</u>.

1) When it's heated, <u>copper</u> reacts with oxygen in the air to make copper(II) oxide — so the reaction <u>uses up oxygen</u>.

2) If you heat an <u>excess</u> of copper in a tube and pass air over it using two <u>syringes</u>, you can use the markers on the syringes to tell <u>how much</u> oxygen has been used up.

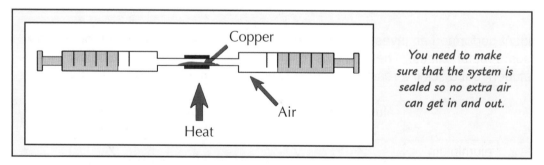

Copper

Heat

Air

You need to make sure that the system is sealed so no extra air can get in and out.

> The chemical equation for the reaction is:
> $$2Cu + O_2 \rightarrow 2CuO$$

3) If you start with <u>100 cm³</u> of air, you'll end up with about <u>80 cm³</u> when the reaction's finished and the air has cooled. If <u>20 cm³</u> of air has gone then <u>around 20%</u> of the air must be oxygen.

Pump those gas syringes...

I think using those <u>syringes</u> is a clever way of calculating how much oxygen is in the air — and you can give your thumbs a workout at the same time. Get this page sussed before turning over.

Oxygen in the Atmosphere

The copper experiment on the previous page isn't the only way to show that the proportion of oxygen in the atmosphere today is around <u>20%</u>. Here are some <u>more lovely experiments</u> for you...

You Can Use **Iron** to **Investigate** the **Proportion** of **Oxygen** in the **Atmosphere**

1) <u>Iron</u> reacts with oxygen in the air to form <u>rust</u> — so iron will <u>remove oxygen</u> from the air.

2) To do this experiment, first soak some <u>iron wool</u> in <u>acetic acid</u> (the acid will catalyse the reaction). Then push the wool into a <u>test tube</u>, put your thumb over the end and invert the tube into a beaker of water.

There's more on the formation of rust on page 67.

3) Over time, the level of the water in the test tube will <u>rise</u>.

4) This is because the iron <u>reacts</u> with the <u>oxygen</u> in the air to make iron oxide. The water rises to fill the space the oxygen took up.

5) To work out the <u>percentage</u> of the air that is oxygen you need to mark the <u>starting</u> and <u>finishing</u> position of the water.

6) Then, <u>fill the tube</u> up to each mark with water and pour the contents into a <u>measuring cylinder</u> to find out the volume of air at the <u>start</u> and the <u>end</u>.

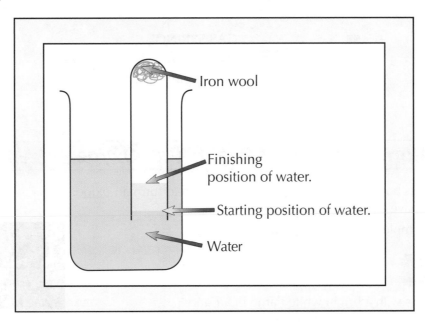

Iron wool

Finishing position of water.

Starting position of water.

Water

7) Use the <u>difference</u> between the start and end volumes to work out the percentage of the <u>starting volume</u> that has been used up — it should be about 20%.

You Can Also Use **Phosphorus**

1) You can do a similar experiment to the one above with <u>white phosphorus</u>.

2) White phosphorus smoulders in air to produce <u>phosphorus oxide</u>.

3) Calculate the amount of oxygen in the air in the same way as for iron.

Oxygen in Reactions

This page has lots of reactions involving oxygen. You need to learn <u>how to prepare it</u> in the lab and how it reacts with other elements to <u>form oxides</u> — i.e. "what happens when you burn something".

You can **Make O$_2$** in the Lab

1) Making pure oxygen in the lab is a <u>cinch</u>. It's made from <u>hydrogen peroxide</u> (H_2O_2).

2) The hydrogen peroxide will <u>decompose</u> (break apart) into <u>water</u> and <u>oxygen</u>. Here's the equation:

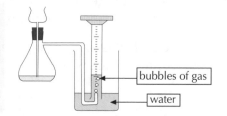

$$2H_2O_{2(aq)} \rightarrow 2H_2O_{(l)} + O_{2(g)}$$

3) This decomposition is really slow but the <u>rate</u> of the reaction can be <u>increased</u> with a sprinkle of <u>manganese(IV) oxide catalyst</u>. The catalyst speeds the reaction up without being used up itself.

4) You can <u>collect</u> the <u>oxygen</u> that's produced <u>over water</u> or by using a <u>gas syringe</u>:

<u>COLLECTION OVER WATER</u>
You can use a delivery tube to <u>bubble</u> the gas into an upside-down measuring cylinder or gas jar filled with <u>water</u>.

bubbles of gas

water

This method only works for <u>insoluble</u> gases otherwise the gas just <u>dissolves</u> in the water.

<u>GAS SYRINGE</u>
You can use a <u>gas syringe</u> to collect pretty much <u>any</u> gas.

When you **Burn** Something it **Reacts** with **Oxygen** in Air

When an element is burnt in air it <u>reacts</u> with the oxygen to form an <u>oxide</u>. These oxides can have either <u>acidic</u> or <u>basic</u> character.

Here are some examples you need to <u>know</u>:

Magnesium

Magnesium burns with a <u>bright white flame</u> in air and the <u>white powder</u> that is formed is <u>magnesium oxide</u>.
Magnesium oxide is slightly <u>alkaline</u> when it's dissolved in water.

$$2Mg_{(s)} + O_{2(g)} \rightarrow 2MgO_{(s)}$$

Carbon

Carbon will burn in air if it's <u>very strongly heated</u>.
It has an orangey/yellowy flame and it produces <u>carbon dioxide</u> gas.
Carbon dioxide is slightly <u>acidic</u> when it's dissolved in water.

$$C_{(s)} + O_{2(g)} \rightarrow CO_{2(g)}$$

Sulfur

<u>Sulfur</u> burns in air or oxygen with a <u>pale blue flame</u> and produces <u>sulfur dioxide</u>.
Sulfur dioxide is <u>acidic</u> when it's dissolved in water.

$$S_{(s)} + O_{2(g)} \rightarrow SO_{2(g)}$$

Preparation of Carbon Dioxide

Here are two ways of <u>producing CO₂</u> in the lab — and you need to know about <u>both</u> of them. But first, a bit of detail on some more methods of collecting gases...

You Can **Collect Gases** in a **Test Tube**

You can collect gases inside a <u>test tube</u> full of <u>air</u>. This works because the gas you're collecting <u>displaces</u> the air in the tube. There are two ways that this can be done: <u>upward delivery</u> and <u>downward delivery</u>.

This all depends on the <u>density</u> of the gas relative to the density of <u>air</u>.

1) The delivery tube is fed directly into a test tube either <u>upwards</u> or <u>downwards</u>.
2) Use <u>upward delivery</u> to collect '<u>lighter than air</u>' gases (e.g. H_2).
3) Use <u>downward delivery</u> to collect '<u>heavier than air</u>' gases (e.g. CO_2, Cl_2).

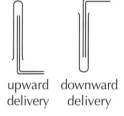

upward   downward
delivery delivery

Dilute Acid reacts with Calcium Carbonate to Produce CO₂

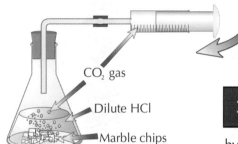

CO$_2$ gas

Dilute HCl

Marble chips

1) The <u>calcium carbonate</u> (<u>marble chips</u>) is put in the bottom of a flask and <u>dilute hydrochloric acid</u> is added.
2) The dilute HCl <u>reacts</u> with the calcium carbonate to produce <u>calcium chloride</u>, <u>water</u> and <u>carbon dioxide gas</u>.

$$2HCl_{(aq)} + CaCO_{3(s)} \rightarrow CaCl_{2(aq)} + H_2O_{(l)} + CO_{2(g)}$$

hydrochloric acid + calcium carbonate →
                    calcium chloride + water + carbon dioxide

3) The <u>carbon dioxide gas</u> is collected in a <u>gas syringe</u> or using <u>downward delivery</u> (see above).

Thermal Decomposition of Metal Carbonates Also Produces CO₂

1) Another way of making CO_2 is by <u>heating</u> a <u>metal carbonate</u>.
2) This is an example of <u>thermal decomposition</u>, which is when a substance <u>breaks down</u> into simpler substances <u>when heated</u>.
3) <u>Copper(II) carbonate</u> is a <u>green powder</u> that will easily decompose to form <u>carbon dioxide</u> and <u>copper(II) oxide</u> when you heat it.
4) <u>Here's the equation</u> for the thermal decomposition of copper(II) carbonate:

$$CuCO_{3(s)} \rightarrow CuO_{(s)} + CO_{2(g)}$$

copper(II) carbonate → copper oxide + carbon dioxide

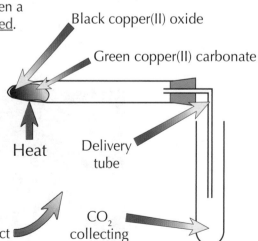

Black copper(II) oxide

Green copper(II) carbonate

Heat

Delivery tube

CO$_2$ collecting

5) To do the experiment, heat <u>copper(II) carbonate</u> then collect the gas that's given off using the <u>downward delivery</u> method.

Carbon Dioxide — the Good and the Bad

Carbon dioxide has some <u>uses</u> (see below), but it can cause a few <u>problems</u> too (see next page).

CO_2 is used in *Fizzy Drinks*...

1) CO_2 is used in <u>carbonated drinks</u> to make them fizzzzzzzzzzzzz.

2) The CO_2 is <u>slightly soluble</u> in water and dissolves into the drinks when under pressure. This produces a <u>slightly acidic solution</u> due to the formation of <u>carbonic acid</u>.

$$CO_{2(g)} \quad + \quad H_2O_{(l)} \quad \rightarrow \quad H_2CO_{3(aq)}$$
$$\text{carbon dioxide} + \text{water} \rightarrow \text{carbonic acid}$$

3) When you open the bottle the <u>bubbles</u> are the CO_2 <u>escaping</u>. If you leave the drink out long enough it will go flat because all the CO_2 escapes.

...and *Fire Extinguishers*

1) Carbon dioxide is also used in <u>fire extinguishers</u>.

2) CO_2 is <u>more dense than air</u> — so it <u>sinks</u> onto the flames and <u>stops</u> the <u>oxygen</u> the fire needs getting to it.

3) Carbon dioxide fire extinguishers are used when water extinguishers <u>aren't</u> safe, for example when putting out <u>electrical fires</u>.

Carbon Dioxide is a *Greenhouse Gas*

1) The <u>temperature</u> of the Earth is a <u>balance</u> between the heat it gets from the Sun and the heat it radiates back out into space.

2) Gases in the <u>atmosphere</u> like <u>carbon dioxide</u>, <u>methane</u> and <u>water vapour</u> naturally act like an <u>insulating layer</u>. They are often called '<u>greenhouse gases</u>'.

3) They absorb most of the heat that would normally be radiated out into space, and re-radiate it in all directions — including back towards the Earth.

Carbon Dioxide — the Good and the Bad

As you saw on the previous page, carbon dioxide is a <u>greenhouse gas</u>. It helps to trap heat from the Sun in the Earth's atmosphere and keep the Earth <u>warm</u>. But the level of carbon dioxide in the atmosphere is <u>increasing</u> and that's causing the planet to get a bit <u>too warm</u>. Read on...

Carbon Dioxide in the Atmosphere is Increasing

1) <u>Human activity</u> affects the <u>amount of carbon dioxide</u> in the atmosphere — examples include:

> - <u>Deforestation</u>: fewer trees means less CO_2 is removed from the atmosphere via photosynthesis.
> - <u>Burning fossil fuels</u>: carbon that was 'locked up' in these fuels is being released as CO_2.

2) It is because of this human activity that over the last 200 years or so, the concentration of carbon dioxide in the atmosphere has been increasing.

3) For this to have happened, CO_2 must be being <u>released</u> into the air <u>faster</u> than it's being <u>removed</u> — this is linked to climate change (see below).

Increasing Carbon Dioxide is Linked to Climate Change

1) There's a <u>correlation</u> between increasing levels of carbon dioxide and the gradual <u>heating up</u> of the Earth's atmosphere (<u>global warming</u>).

2) Although the Earth's temperature varies naturally, there's a <u>scientific consensus</u> that the extra carbon dioxide has <u>caused</u> the average <u>temperature</u> of the Earth to <u>increase</u>.

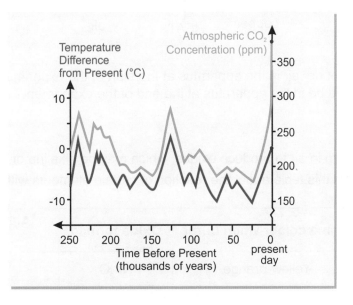

3) Global warming is a type of <u>climate change</u> and causes other types of climate change, e.g. changing rainfall patterns. It could also cause severe <u>flooding</u> due to the polar ice caps melting and <u>sea level rise</u>.

Problems, problems — there's always summat goin' wrong...

A <u>certain amount</u> of carbon dioxide in the atmosphere is useful. It helps to keep the Earth warm and we'd be dead cold without it (and plants need it to grow). But increasing levels of carbon dioxide are gradually <u>heating up</u> the Earth's atmosphere, which could cause all sorts of <u>climate-related problems</u>.

Warm-Up and Exam Questions

I really can't emphasise enough how important it is to work through all these questions. They'll show you exactly what you've learnt and what you haven't, so you know where to focus your revision.

Warm-Up Questions

1) Give the approximate percentages of the following gases in the air:
   a) nitrogen   b) oxygen   c) carbon dioxide

2) Describe an experiment you can do with iron wool to show the proportion of oxygen in the air.

3) What type of delivery system would you use to collect gases that are heavier than air?

4) Copy and complete the equation for the production of carbon dioxide from calcium carbonate.
   $CaCO_3 + 2$............................. $\rightarrow CaCl_2 +$ .... $+ CO_2$

Exam Questions

1   The proportion of oxygen in the atmosphere can be found by heating an excess of copper so that it reacts with oxygen in the air to form copper oxide.

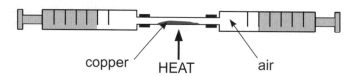

copper   HEAT   air

There was 50 cm³ of dry air in the apparatus at the start of the experiment.
How much air would be in the apparatus at the end of the experiment?

(2 marks)

2   Some elements burn in air to produce oxides, which may be alkaline or acidic.
Copy and complete this table about the reaction of certain elements with oxygen.

Element	Flame colour when burnt	Oxide formed	Acid-base character of oxide
sodium	Yellow-orange	Na_2O	Alkaline
magnesium			Slightly alkaline
carbon	Orange/yellow	CO_2	
sulfur			

(6 marks)

Exam Questions

3   Oxygen can be produced by the decomposition of hydrogen peroxide (H_2O_2).

a)   Write a chemical equation for the decomposition of
hydrogen peroxide, including state symbols.

(2 marks)

b)   An experiment was set up to
investigate which substance
is the most effective catalyst
for the decomposition of
hydrogen peroxide.

Samples of three substances with
the same surface area were added
to hydrogen peroxide solution.

The same volume and
concentration of hydrogen peroxide
was used each time.

The volume of oxygen made over
time was measured and recorded,
and is shown in the graph.

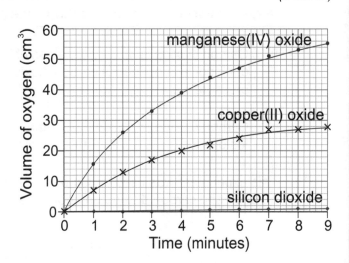

i)   How much oxygen was produced after 3 minutes with copper(II) oxide?
Give your answer in cm^3.

(1 mark)

ii)   Suggest how the oxygen could be collected and measured in this experiment.

(1 mark)

iii) State, with a reason, the most effective catalyst.

(2 marks)

4   Heating a metal carbonate, such as copper(II) carbonate, produces carbon dioxide.
This can be done in the laboratory and the carbon dioxide can be collected in a test tube.
The apparatus shown below could be used to perform this experiment.

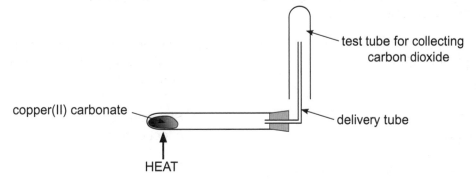

a)   The apparatus in the diagram has been set up incorrectly.
Describe **one** change you would need to make in order to collect
carbon dioxide and explain why this change is necessary.

(2 marks)

b)   Apart from carbon dioxide, what other product is made in this reaction?

(1 mark)

c)   What is the name for the type of reaction where a substance is heated and breaks
down to produce two or more products?

(1 mark)

Exam Questions

5   Carbon dioxide has many useful properties.

a)   Copy and complete the sentences about the uses of carbon dioxide, using words from the box below. Each word can be used once, more than once, or not at all.

| larger   denser   oxygen   coating   very   lighter   released   hydrogen   slightly |

i)   Carbon dioxide is .... soluble in water. The bubbling when a fizzy drink bottle is opened is carbon dioxide escaping from the drink when the pressure is ....

(2 marks)

ii)   Carbon dioxide is .... than air. It is used in some fire extinguishers. It stops the .... that the fire needs getting to the flames.

(2 marks)

b)   This experiment was used to compare the effects of nitrogen and carbon dioxide on heat radiation.

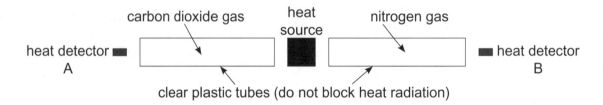

carbon dioxide gas   heat source   nitrogen gas

heat detector ▪   ▪ heat detector
A   B

clear plastic tubes (do not block heat radiation)

State which detector will detect more heat from the heat source. Explain your choice.

(2 marks)

c)   Explain the effect of atmospheric carbon dioxide on heat radiated from the Earth's surface.

(2 marks)

d)   These graphs show how the atmospheric CO_2 level and temperature changed over time.

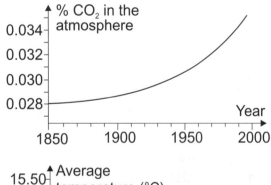

i)   Describe the overall trend in the Earth's temperature between 1850 and 2000.

(1 mark)

ii)   State **one** possible effect of this trend.

(1 mark)

Tests for Cations

Forensic science involves a lot of <u>chemical tests</u>, which is what these next pages are about. Before you start reading, you have to pretend you have a <u>mystery substance</u>. You don't know what it is, but you need to find out — just like that bloke off the telly who investigates murders.

First off, some tests for <u>cations</u> (positive ions — such as Na^+ or Ca^{2+}).

Flame Tests Identify Metal Ions

Compounds of some metals burn with a <u>characteristic colour</u> (as you see every November 5th).

So you can test for various metal ions by heating your substance and seeing whether it <u>burns</u> with a <u>distinctive colour flame</u>.

> <u>Lithium</u>, Li^+, burns with a crimson-red flame.
> <u>Sodium</u>, Na^+, burns with an yellow-orange flame.
> <u>Potassium</u>, K^+, burns with a lilac flame.
> <u>Calcium</u>, Ca^{2+}, burns with a brick-red flame.

To do the test you need to <u>clean</u> a <u>platinum</u> wire loop by dipping it in some dilute <u>HCl</u> and then holding it in a <u>flame</u>. Once you hold the loop in the flame and it burns <u>without any colour</u> you can dip it into the <u>sample</u> you want to test, then put it back in the flame. Then say ooooo and ahhhhh.

Some Metals Form a Coloured Precipitate with NaOH

This is also a test for metal ions, but it's slightly more involved. Concentrate now...

1) Many <u>metal hydroxides</u> are <u>insoluble</u> and precipitate out of solution when formed. Some of these hydroxides have a <u>characteristic colour</u>.

2) So in this test you add a few drops of <u>sodium hydroxide</u> solution to a solution of your mystery compound in a test tube — all in the hope of forming an insoluble hydroxide.

3) If you get a <u>coloured insoluble hydroxide</u> you can then tell which metal was in the compound.

Metal ion	Colour of precipitate	Ionic Reaction
Copper(II), Cu^{2+}	Blue	$Cu^{2+}(aq) + 2OH^-(aq) \rightarrow Cu(OH)_2(s)$
Iron(II), Fe^{2+}	Sludgy green	$Fe^{2+}(aq) + 2OH^-(aq) \rightarrow Fe(OH)_2(s)$
Iron(III), Fe^{3+}	Reddish brown	$Fe^{3+}(aq) + 3OH^-(aq) \rightarrow Fe(OH)_3(s)$

"Ammonium Compound + NaOH" Gives Off (Stinky) Ammonia

1) <u>Ammonia gas</u> (NH_3) is smelly — it reeks of <u>cat wee</u>. You can usually tell if there's some about, but it's not a good idea to smell it deliberately as it can be really <u>harmful to your eyes</u> — not cool.

2) You can <u>check for ammonia gas</u> using a damp piece of <u>red litmus paper</u>. If there's ammonia present, the paper will turn <u>blue</u>.

3) You can use this to <u>test</u> whether a substance contains <u>ammonium ions</u> (NH_4^+). Add some <u>sodium hydroxide</u> to a solution of your mystery substance in a test tube. If there's ammonia given off this means there are ammonium ions in your mystery substance.

The litmus paper needs to be damp so the ammonia gas can dissolve and make the colour change.

Tests for Anions

It's not just positive ions you can test for, you'll be pleased to know.
Yep, you can also test for _negative ions_. So the fun goes on...

Hydrochloric Acid Can Help Detect _Carbonates_

1) To test for carbonates, add dilute hydrochloric acid (HCl) to your test sample.
   If carbonates (CO_3^{2-}) are present then carbon dioxide will be released.

   Carbonates give off CO_2 with HCl

   $$CO_3^{2-}{}_{(s)} + 2H^+{}_{(aq)} \rightarrow CO_{2(g)} + H_2O_{(l)}$$

   carbonate + acid → _carbon dioxide + water_

2) You can test for carbon dioxide using limewater — see the next page.

Test for _Sulfates_ with HCl and _Barium Chloride_

Sulfate ions (SO_4^{2-}) produce a white precipitate

1) To test for a sulfate ion (SO_4^{2-}), add dilute HCl, followed by barium chloride solution, $BaCl_2$.

   $$Ba^{2+}{}_{(aq)} + SO_4^{2-}{}_{(aq)} \rightarrow BaSO_{4(s)}$$

2) A white precipitate of barium sulfate means the original compound was a sulfate.

3) The hydrochloric acid is added to get rid of any traces of carbonate or sulfite ions before you do the test. Both of these would also produce a precipitate, so they'd confuse the results.

Test for _Halides_ (_Cl⁻_, _Br⁻_, _I⁻_) with Nitric Acid and _Silver Nitrate_

1) To test for chloride, bromide or iodide ions, add dilute nitric acid (HNO_3),
   followed by silver nitrate solution ($AgNO_3$).

   $Ag^+{}_{(aq)} + Cl^-{}_{(aq)} \longrightarrow AgCl_{(s)}$ A chloride ion gives a white precipitate of silver chloride.

   $Ag^+{}_{(aq)} + Br^-{}_{(aq)} \longrightarrow AgBr_{(s)}$ A bromide ion gives a cream precipitate of silver bromide.

   $Ag^+{}_{(aq)} + I^-{}_{(aq)} \longrightarrow AgI_{(s)}$ An iodide ion gives a yellow precipitate of silver iodide.

2) Again, the acid is added to get rid of carbonate or sulfite ions before the test.
   You use nitric acid in this test, though, not HCl.

These tests assume that your mystery substance is ionic...

...which it might not be. But you might be able to tell — ionic substances tend to be crystalline solids with a high melting point. So if it's a gas, volatile liquid or soft solid, no need to bother with these tests.

Tests for Gases

There are lots of clever ways of testing for <u>different gases</u>, so get learning the ones below.

There are **Tests** for **5 Common Gases**

1) Chlorine

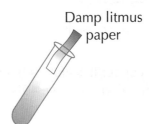
Damp litmus paper

Chlorine <u>bleaches</u> damp <u>litmus paper</u>, turning it white. (It may turn <u>red</u> for a moment first though — that's because a solution of chlorine is <u>acidic</u>.)

2) Oxygen

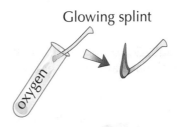
Glowing splint

Oxygen <u>relights</u> a <u>glowing splint</u>.

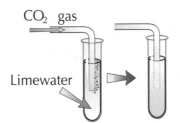
CO_2 gas

Limewater

3) Carbon Dioxide

Carbon dioxide <u>turns limewater cloudy</u> — just bubble the gas through a test tube of limewater and watch what happens.

4) Hydrogen

Hydrogen makes a "<u>squeaky pop</u>" with a <u>lighted splint</u>. (The noise comes from the hydrogen burning with the oxygen in the air to form H_2O.)

Squeaky pop!
Squeaky pop!
H_2 gas

5) Ammonia

ammonia

Ammonia <u>turns</u> damp <u>red litmus paper blue</u>. (It also has a very strong <u>smell</u>.)

These are all dead useful tests to know...

So, if you want to test for <u>chlorine</u> or <u>ammonia</u> you need litmus paper, for <u>oxygen</u> or <u>hydrogen</u> you need a splint, and for <u>carbon dioxide</u> you need limewater. What could be simpler.

Tests for Water

Dipping your finger in a liquid and saying "it's wet" is not the best test for water.
Don't worry though, there's a more scientific method for that too...

*Wet Copper(II) Sulfate is **Blue** — **Dry** Copper(II) Sulfate is **White***

Copper(II) sulfate crystals can be used as a test for water.

1) When copper(II) sulfate is bound to water (water of crystallisation, see page 40) it forms lovely blue crystals.

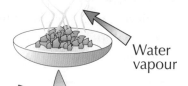
Water vapour

2) If you heat the blue hydrated copper(II) sulfate crystals it drives the water off.

3) This leaves a white anhydrous copper(II) sulfate powder, which doesn't have any water bound to it.

Hydrated means with water.
Anhydrous means without water.

4) If you then add a couple of drops of water to the white powder you get the blue crystals back again.

So, if you want to test for water, all you need to do is add anhydrous copper(II) sulfate and see if the white powder turns blue.

This test will tell you if water is present in a solution but it won't tell you if the water is pure.

Checking the **Purity** of **Water**

1) When a sample is pure it means it's only made up of one substance.

2) This means it has set defined physical properties like boiling point and freezing point.

3) Pure water will always:

Boil at 100 °C
Freeze at 0 °C

4) If you find the boiling point isn't 100 °C or freezing point isn't 0 °C then the sample isn't pure.

Blue copper(II) sulfate crystals contain water

This 'hydrated'/'anhydrous' malarkey has turned up before — see page 40 if you don't believe me. As always, cover up the page and scribble down what you know. Unlike with all those tests for cations and anions (pages 79 and 80) there are only two colours you need to remember here: blue and white. So all in all getting this lot learnt should be a pretty straightforward job.

Warm-Up and Exam Questions

We're nearly at the end of the section now. Make sure you answer all these questions first though.

Warm-Up Questions

1) A compound burns with a crimson-red flame. What metal ion does it contain?
2) a) Describe a test to identify ammonia gas.
   b) How does this test allow you to test for ammonium ions?
3) Describe the test for chlorine gas.
4) What colour are hydrated copper(II) sulfate crystals?

Exam Questions

1   Potassium chloride is used to replace some of the sodium chloride in low-sodium table salt.
     A flame test can be used to tell the difference between potassium chloride and sodium chloride.

   a)   Describe how to carry out a flame test.

                                                                                    (2 marks)

   b)   Explain how you could tell from a flame test that a substance was potassium
        chloride and not sodium chloride.

                                                                                    (2 marks)

   c)   Some medicines contain potassium sodium tartrate. Explain why you cannot use a
        flame test to show that these medicines contained potassium.

                                                                                    (2 marks)

2   A student has a sample of an ionic compound and wants
     to find out what negative ions it contains.

   a)   The student wants to test the compound for the presence of sulfate ions.
        i)   State which two reactants are used to test for sulfate ions.

                                                                                    (2 marks)

        ii)   What would be observed after adding these reactants
              to a solution of a sulfate compound?

                                                                                    (1 mark)

   b)   The student tested the compound to see if it contained carbonate ions.
        The student added a solution to the compound, collected the gas
        that it gave off and bubbled the gas through limewater.
        i)   Name the solution that the student added.

                                                                                    (1 mark)

        ii)   The compound is a carbonate. What gas did it give off?

                                                                                    (1 mark)

   c)   The student is given a solution of another compound and told that it contains either
        chloride or bromide ions. Describe a test the student could perform to discover
        which of these ions it contains.

                                                                                    (4 marks)

Exam Questions

3   A student adds a few drops of NaOH solution to solutions of different metal compounds.

a)   Copy and complete her table of results.

Metal ion	Colour of precipitate
Fe^{2+}	
	blue
Fe^{3+}	

(3 marks)

b)   Copy and complete the balanced ionic equation for the reaction of iron(II) ions with hydroxide ions by inserting state symbols.

$$Fe^{2+}_{(\ldots\ldots\ldots)} + 2OH^{-}_{(\ldots\ldots\ldots)} \rightarrow Fe(OH)_{2(\ldots\ldots\ldots)}$$

(1 mark)

c)   Write a balanced ionic equation for the reaction of iron(III) ions with hydroxide ions. Include state symbols.

(3 marks)

4   Electrolysis of water gives hydrogen gas and oxygen gas.

a)   Describe a simple laboratory test that you could use to identify hydrogen gas.

(2 marks)

b)   Describe a simple laboratory test that you could use to identify oxygen gas.

(2 marks)

5   A fuel was burnt in pure oxygen and the products of the combustion reaction were collected.

a)   A liquid condensed out of the products after they were cooled to room temperature. The liquid was added to anhydrous copper(II) sulfate.

     i)   State the colour of anhydrous copper(II) sulfate powder.

(1 mark)

     ii)   State the colour change that would take place if the liquid contained water.

(1 mark)

b)   The test with anhydrous copper(II) sulfate indicated that the liquid contained water. Next, the liquid's freezing point and boiling point were found.

     Freezing point: −4 °C   **Boiling point:** 106 °C

Explain what these results show.

(3 marks)

c)   The gas that was produced by the burning fuel was also tested. The gas did not bleach damp litmus paper. When the gas was bubbled through limewater, the limewater turned cloudy. Explain what these results show.

(4 marks)

Revision Summary for Section 2

It's the end of the section, which can mean only one thing — it's quiz time. Below are a wonderful selection of questions designed to make sure all the important info sticks in your brain.

1) What are the rows on the periodic table called?
   What are the columns on the periodic table called?

2) Why are the noble gases inert?

3) Name the gas that is produced when an alkali metal reacts with water.

4) Write the word equation for the reaction between sodium and water.

5) Describe how the reactivity of alkali metals changes as you go down the group.

6) How does the boiling point of the halogens change as the atomic number increases?

7) Describe how the reactivity of the halogens changes as you go up the group.

8) What's hydrogen chloride called when it's in aqueous solution?

9) Describe what happens when hydrogen chloride is added to water. What is this process called?

10) Explain why HCl in methylbenzene is not acidic.

11) What is a displacement reaction?

12) If you mix chlorine water with potassium bromide solution, what colour will it go?

13) If you mix bromine water with potassium iodide solution, what colour will it go?

14) What does OIL RIG stand for?

15) Write the word equation for the reaction of an acid with a metal.

16) Put these metals in order from most reactive to least reactive when added to dilute acid:
    aluminium, iron, magnesium and zinc.

17) Give the name of:
    a) a very reactive metal,
    b) a not at all reactive metal.

18)* What happens when copper oxide reacts with magnesium?

19)* What happens when an aluminium rod is put in a solution of zinc sulfate?

20) Write out the word equation for iron rusting.

21) Describe two ways that rusting can be prevented.

22) What percentage of the atmosphere is oxygen?

23) Describe an experiment to prepare oxygen that can be carried out in a lab.

24) Describe the reaction of oxygen with magnesium.

25) Give two ways of preparing carbon dioxide in the lab.

26) Give two uses of carbon dioxide.

27) Explain the link between carbon dioxide and global warming.

28) What colour flame does potassium burn with?

29) What colour precipitate do iron(II) compounds form with sodium hydroxide?

30) Give the name of an acid which can be used to test for the presence of carbonate ions.

31) What colour is the precipitate formed when a bromide ion
    reacts with dilute nitric acid and silver nitrate?

32) What is the test for carbon dioxide?

33) What is the test for hydrogen gas?

34) What colour are the crystals of copper(II) sulfate that form in the presence of water?

35) How can you tell if a sample of water is pure?

* Answers on page 193.

Alkanes

A new page and a new section. This one's all about <u>organic chemistry</u>. That just means it's about molecules that contain <u>carbon</u>.

Alkanes are **Hydrocarbons**

1) <u>Hydrocarbons</u> are molecules that are made up of <u>hydrogen</u> and <u>carbon</u> atoms <u>only</u>.

2) Alkanes are hydrocarbons — they're <u>chains of carbon atoms</u> surrounded by <u>hydrogen atoms</u>.

3) Different alkanes have chains of different <u>lengths</u>.

4) You need to know the <u>names</u> and the <u>displayed formulas</u> of the first five alkanes.

The displayed formula is a picture of the molecule drawn with all the bonds shown.

$$H-\overset{\displaystyle H}{\underset{\displaystyle H}{C}}-\overset{\displaystyle H}{\underset{\displaystyle H}{C}}-\overset{\displaystyle H}{\underset{\displaystyle H}{C}}-\overset{\displaystyle H}{\underset{\displaystyle H}{C}}-H$$

1) *Methane*

Formula: CH_4

(natural gas)

$$H-\overset{\displaystyle H}{\underset{\displaystyle H}{C}}-H$$

2) *Ethane*

Formula: C_2H_6

$$H-\overset{\displaystyle H}{\underset{\displaystyle H}{C}}-\overset{\displaystyle H}{\underset{\displaystyle H}{C}}-H$$

3) *Propane*

Formula: C_3H_8

$$H-\overset{\displaystyle H}{\underset{\displaystyle H}{C}}-\overset{\displaystyle H}{\underset{\displaystyle H}{C}}-\overset{\displaystyle H}{\underset{\displaystyle H}{C}}-H$$

4) *Butane*

Formula: C_4H_{10}

$$H-\overset{\displaystyle H}{\underset{\displaystyle H}{C}}-\overset{\displaystyle H}{\underset{\displaystyle H}{C}}-\overset{\displaystyle H}{\underset{\displaystyle H}{C}}-\overset{\displaystyle H}{\underset{\displaystyle H}{C}}-H$$

5) *Pentane*

Formula: C_5H_{12}

$$H-\overset{\displaystyle H}{\underset{\displaystyle H}{C}}-\overset{\displaystyle H}{\underset{\displaystyle H}{C}}-\overset{\displaystyle H}{\underset{\displaystyle H}{C}}-\overset{\displaystyle H}{\underset{\displaystyle H}{C}}-\overset{\displaystyle H}{\underset{\displaystyle H}{C}}-H$$

To help remember the names of the first four alkanes just remember:
<u>M</u>ice <u>E</u>at <u>P</u>eanut <u>B</u>utter.
Pentane is five, just like a pentagon, so you'll have to remember that one on its own.

Alkanes

The alkanes have a <u>general formula</u>, so you can work out the <u>molecular formula</u> of any alkane as long as you know how many carbons it's got. There's a pattern for what happens when they <u>burn</u>, too.

Alkanes are a **Homologous Series**

1) The alkanes on the previous page are part of a <u>homologous series</u>.

2) A homologous series is a <u>group of compounds</u> that can all be represented by the <u>same general formula</u>.

3) You can use a general formula to work out the <u>molecular formula</u> of <u>any member</u> of a homologous series.

4) Alkanes all have the <u>general formula</u>:

$$\text{Alkanes} = C_nH_{2n+2}$$

5) So if an alkane has <u>4 carbons</u> (butane), it's got to have $(2\times4)+2 = \underline{10 \text{ hydrogens}}$.

6) A carbon atom can form <u>four covalent bonds</u> and a hydrogen atom can only form <u>one covalent bond</u> (see pages 25-27). The diagrams of the alkanes on the previous page show that all the carbon atoms have formed four bonds and all the hydrogen atoms have formed one bond — a line represents each covalent bond.

7) No more atoms can join onto the carbon atoms so the alkanes are <u>saturated</u>.

Complete Combustion Happens When There's Plenty of **Oxygen**

When there's <u>plenty of oxygen</u> about, alkanes burn to produce <u>carbon dioxide</u> and <u>water</u>.

alkane + oxygen → carbon dioxide + water   (+ energy)

1) <u>Complete combustion</u> releases <u>lots of energy</u> and only produces those two <u>harmless waste products</u>. When there's <u>plenty of oxygen</u> and combustion is complete, the gas burns with a <u>clean blue flame</u>.

Lots of CO_2 isn't ideal, but the alternatives are worse (see the next page).

2) Here's the <u>balanced equation</u> for the complete combustion of <u>methane</u>, a <u>hydrocarbon fuel</u>.

$$CH_4 + 2O_2 \rightarrow CO_2 + 2H_2O$$

Make sure you end up with the <u>same number</u> of Cs, Hs and Os on <u>either side</u> of the arrow.

3) Many <u>heaters</u> that burn <u>methane</u> (natural gas) release the <u>waste gases</u> into the room, which is perfectly OK. As long as the gas heater is <u>working properly</u> and the room is <u>well ventilated</u>, there's no problem.

Double the number of carbon atoms, plus two...

... to give you the number of hydrogen atoms in <u>any</u> alkane. It works every time, so memorise that general formula. Also remember the products of complete combustion — <u>carbon dioxide</u> and <u>water</u>.

More Alkanes

You saw complete combustion on the previous page, so now for <u>incomplete combustion</u>...

Incomplete Combustion of Alkanes is NOT Safe

1) If there <u>isn't enough oxygen</u>, alkane combustion will be <u>incomplete</u>. Carbon dioxide and water are still produced, but you can also get <u>carbon</u> and <u>carbon monoxide</u> (CO), which is a poisonous gas (see p. 136).

> alkane + oxygen → carbon + carbon monoxide + carbon dioxide + water

(+ energy)

2) Incomplete combustion means a <u>smoky yellow flame</u>, and <u>less energy</u> than complete combustion.

3) Here's an example of an <u>equation</u> for incomplete combustion.

> $4CH_4 + 6O_2 \rightarrow C + 2CO + CO_2 + 8H_2O$

This is just <u>one possibility</u>. The products depend on how much oxygen is present...

... e.g. you could also have:
$4CH_4 + 7O_2 \rightarrow 2CO + 2CO_2 + 8H_2O$
— but the equation has to be <u>balanced</u>.

Halogens React with Alkanes to make Haloalkanes

1) <u>Chlorine</u> and <u>bromine</u> react with alkanes in the presence of <u>ultraviolet light</u>.

2) In these reactions a <u>hydrogen</u> atom from the alkane is <u>substituted</u> (replaced) by <u>chlorine</u> or <u>bromine</u>. So this is called a <u>substitution reaction</u>.

3) This is how bromine and methane react together to form <u>bromomethane</u>.

methane + bromine → bromomethane + hydrogen bromide

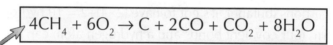

The UV here shows that the reaction needs ultraviolet light.

A few more reactions to learn here...

Make sure you understand what's going on in these reactions — what the conditions are (not enough oxygen for incomplete combustion or UV light for halogen reactions) and what's produced from them.

Alkenes

Alkenes are a type of hydrocarbon. They're different from alkanes because they contain <u>double bonds</u>.

Alkenes Have a C=C Double Bond

1) Alkenes are hydrocarbons which have a <u>double bond</u> between two of the <u>carbon</u> atoms in their chain.

2) They are <u>unsaturated</u> molecules because they <u>can make more bonds</u> — the double bond can open up, allowing the two carbon atoms to bond with other atoms (see the next page).

3) The first three alkenes are <u>ethene</u> (with two carbon atoms) <u>propene</u> (three Cs) and <u>butene</u> (four Cs).

4) <u>All alkenes</u> have the general formula: C_nH_{2n}
   — they have twice as many hydrogens as carbons.

$$\text{Alkenes} = C_nH_{2n}$$

1) Ethene

<u>Formula</u>: C_2H_4

Hydrogen atoms only make one bond.

This is a double bond — so each carbon atom is still making four bonds.

2) Propene

<u>Formula</u>: C_3H_6

3) Butene

<u>Formula</u>: C_4H_8

H–C–C=C–C–H   or

There are <u>two</u> different structures for butene (C_4H_8) — the double bond can be in two different places.

When two molecules have <u>identical molecular formulas</u> but <u>different structures</u> they are called <u>isomers</u>.

That double bond makes all the difference...

Don't get alkenes confused with alkanes. Alkenes have a C=C bond, alkanes don't. The first part of their names is the same though. "<u>Meth-</u>" means "<u>one</u> carbon atom", "<u>eth-</u>" means "<u>two</u> C atoms", "<u>prop-</u>" means "<u>three</u> C atoms", "<u>but-</u>" means "<u>four</u> C atoms", etc.

More Alkenes

Now that you've met some alkenes, it's time to learn about some of their <u>reactions</u>.
It's all down to the double bond splitting...

Halogens React with Alkenes, Forming Haloalkanes

1) <u>Halogens</u> can react with alkenes to make <u>haloalkanes</u>.

2) For example bromine and ethene react together to form <u>dibromoethane</u>.

ethene + bromine → dibromoethane

$$H_2C=CH_2 + Br_2 \longrightarrow H-CBr_2-CBr_2-H$$

There are two bromine atoms so it's called dibromoethane.

3) These are called <u>addition reactions</u> because the C=C double bond is split and a halogen atom is <u>added</u> to each of the carbons.

Alkenes Turn Bromine Water Colourless

1) The reaction between bromine and alkenes is often used as a <u>test</u> for carbon-carbon double bonds.

2) When you shake an alkene with <u>orange bromine water</u>, the solution becomes <u>colourless</u> — this is because the <u>bromine</u> molecules, which are <u>orange</u>, are reacting with the <u>alkene</u> to make a <u>dibromoalkane</u>, which is <u>colourless</u>.

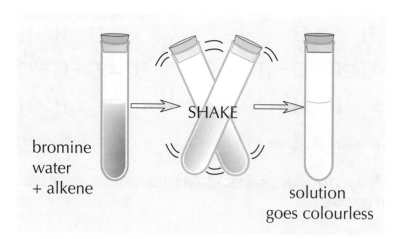

bromine water + alkene

SHAKE

solution goes colourless

A few more reactions to learn here...

If you've got an alkane and an alkene, and you want to know which is which, then doing a quick test with bromine water will give you your answer. With the alkane, the bromine water will <u>stay orange</u>.

Ethanol

Ethanol is the alcohol in beer and wine. <u>Ethanol</u> can be made using <u>ethene</u>, or by the <u>fermentation of sugar</u>. You need to know about both methods, so read on.

Ethanol Can Be Produced from **Ethene** *and* **Steam**

1) <u>Ethene</u> is produced from <u>crude oil</u> (by cracking — see page 137).

2) Ethene (C_2H_4) will react with <u>steam</u> (H_2O) to make <u>ethanol</u>.

3) The reaction needs a <u>temperature</u> of 300 °C and a <u>pressure</u> of 60-70 atmospheres.

4) <u>Phosphoric acid</u> is used as a <u>catalyst</u>.

$$C_2H_4 + H_2O \rightarrow C_2H_5OH$$

5) At the moment this is a <u>cheap</u> process, because ethene's fairly <u>cheap</u> and <u>not much</u> of it is <u>wasted</u>.

6) The trouble is that <u>crude oil</u> is a <u>non-renewable</u> resource, which will start running out fairly soon. This means that using ethene to make ethanol will become very <u>expensive</u>.

Ethanol Can Also Be Produced by **Fermentation**

The alcohol in beer and wine etc. isn't made from ethene — it's made by <u>fermentation</u>.

1) The raw material for fermentation is <u>sugar</u> e.g. glucose. This is converted into <u>ethanol</u> using <u>yeast</u>.

2) This process needs a <u>lower temperature</u> (about 30 °C) and <u>simpler equipment</u> than when using ethene.

3) Another advantage is that the raw materials are all <u>renewable resources</u>. <u>Sugar</u> (sugar cane) is <u>grown</u> as a major crop in several parts of the world, including many poorer countries. <u>Yeast</u> is also easy to grow.

4) There are <u>disadvantages</u> though. The ethanol you get from this process <u>isn't very concentrated</u>, so it needs to be <u>distilled</u> to increase its strength (as in whisky distilleries). It also needs to be <u>purified</u>.

Paper 2

More Ethanol

The methods of ethanol production that you learnt about on the previous page have pros and cons. Nothing's ever straightforward...

Both Methods have *Advantages* and *Disadvantages*...

You need to know the <u>factors</u> that affect which method you use to produce ethanol. Here's a quick summary:

Method	Ethene + steam	Fermentation
Rate of Reaction	Very fast	Very slow
Quality of Product	Pure	Very impure — needs further processing
Raw Material	Ethene from oil — a finite resource	Sugar — a renewable resource
Process/Costs	Continuous process at high temp and pressure, so expensive equipment needed, but low labour costs.	Batch process at lower temp, so cheap equipment needed, but high labour costs.

Ethanol can be *Dehydrated* to Form *Ethene*

1) You can also turn ethanol <u>back into</u> ethene.

2) This is done by <u>removing water</u> from the ethanol in a <u>dehydration reaction</u> (i.e. elimination of water).

$$H-\overset{\displaystyle H}{\underset{\displaystyle H}{C}}-\overset{\displaystyle H}{\underset{\displaystyle H}{C}}-O-H \longrightarrow \overset{H}{\underset{H}{C}}=\overset{H}{\underset{H}{C}} + H_2O$$

$$C_2H_5OH \rightarrow C_2H_4 + H_2O$$

3) <u>Ethanol vapour</u> is passed over a hot <u>catalyst</u> of <u>aluminium oxide</u>, Al_2O_3 — the catalyst provides a large surface area for the reaction.

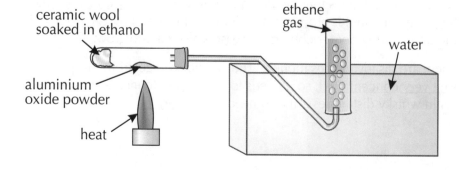

ceramic wool soaked in ethanol

aluminium oxide powder

heat

ethene gas

water

Warm-Up and Exam Questions

It's that time again... See what you've learnt with this set of questions.

Warm-Up Questions

1) Name the first five alkanes.
2) When does complete combustion happen?
3) What is the general formula of the alkenes?
4) Why are alkenes described as unsaturated hydrocarbons?
5) Why are alkenes able to react with halogens?
6) What will happen if you add propene to bromine water?
7) Give two ways of making ethanol.

Exam Questions

1   Alkanes are a group of hydrocarbon compounds.
   a)   State what is meant by the term hydrocarbon.

   (2 marks)

   b)   i)   State the general formula of the alkanes.

   (1 mark)

   ii)   Give the term for a group of compounds that can be represented
         by the same general formula.

   (1 mark)

   c)   Draw the displayed formula of butane.

   (1 mark)

   d)   Methane will react with bromine in the presence of UV light.
        Complete the word equation for this reaction.

   methane + bromine $\xrightarrow{\text{UV}}$ .... + ...

   (2 marks)

2   The storage tank pictured below contains butane, a saturated hydrocarbon.

   a)   Explain what it means when a molecule is saturated.

   (1 mark)

   b)   i)   Complete the chemical equation for the complete
            combustion of butane.

   ....C_4H_{10} + ... → .... + ...

   (2 marks)

   ii)   What other two products could be formed if
         butane undergoes incomplete combustion?

   (2 marks)

Exam Questions

3 Complete the table to show the missing information for the two alkenes given.

Name of alkene	Formula	Displayed formula
ethene		
	C_3H_6	

(4 marks)

PAPER 2

4 Ethanol can be used to make ethene.

a) Write a chemical equation for the conversion of ethanol into ethene.

(1 mark)

b) State the name for this type of reaction.

(1 mark)

c) Identify a suitable catalyst for this reaction.

(1 mark)

PAPER 2

5 Two different methods can be used to manufacture ethanol.
The incomplete table below shows some information about the two methods.

a) Complete the table.

Method	Reaction	Temperature Needed	Problems
A	$C_2H_4 + \text{.....................} \rightarrow C_2H_5OH$		Expensive equipment
B	$C_6H_{12}O_6 \rightarrow 2CO_2 + \text{..........}C_2H_5OH$		Labour-intensive

(4 marks)

b) What type of reaction occurs in method **B**?

(1 mark)

c) Method **A** requires a high temperature.
State the pressure and type of catalyst that are typically used in the reaction.

(2 marks)

d) Country Z has a good supply of crude oil and has a very cold climate.

Suggest which method, A or B, would be most suitable for manufacturing ethanol in country Z. Give a reason for your answer.

(2 marks)

Revision Summary for Section 3

Some people skip these pages. But what's the point in reading the section if you're not going to check if you really know it or not. Each of these questions is carefully crafted to make sure you really did read all of those pages — just read the first ten questions and I guarantee there'll be an answer you'll have to look up. Keep trying till you can do them all without having to look back at the section. When it comes to the exam, you'll be glad you did.

1) What type of molecule is an alkane?
2) What is the name of this alkane?

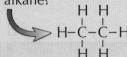

3) Draw the displayed formula of propane.
4) What is a homologous series?
5) What does saturated mean?
6) Write out the word equation for the complete combustion of an alkane.
7) Write out the balanced equation for the complete combustion of methane.
8) Write out the word equation for the incomplete combustion of an alkane.
9) Does complete or incomplete combustion produce more energy?
10) a) Write out the equation for the reaction between methane and bromine in the presence of UV light.
    b) Give the names of the products of this reaction.
11) What is the main feature of an alkene?
12) What's the name of this alkene?

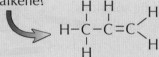

13) Draw the two possible structures of butene.
14) What is the name given to two molecules with identical molecular formulas but different structures?
15) What's the name of the type of reaction that happens between a halogen and an alkene?
16) a) Write out the equation for the reaction between ethene and bromine.
    b) Explain how you can use this reaction to test for carbon-carbon double bonds.
17) a) Write out the equation for the reaction between ethene and steam to make ethanol.
    b) What temperature and pressure does this reaction need?
    c) What is the catalyst that's used for this reaction?
18) a) In fermentation, what converts the sugar into ethanol?
    b) What temperature does this reaction need?
19) a) Write out the equation for the dehydration of ethanol to make ethene.
    b) What is the catalyst that's used for this reaction?

Acids and Alkalis

To test the pH of a solution, you can use an <u>indicator</u> — and that means <u>colours</u>...

The pH Scale Goes from 0 to 14

1) The <u>strongest acid</u> has <u>pH 0</u>. The <u>strongest alkali</u> has <u>pH 14</u>.

2) A <u>neutral</u> substance has <u>pH 7</u> (e.g. pure water).

| Strongly acidic | | | Weakly acidic | | | Weakly alkaline | | | Strongly alkaline |

pH 0   1   2   3   4   5   6   7   8   9   10   11   12   13   14

← ACIDS | NEUTRAL ALKALIS →

car battery acid, stomach acid | vinegar, lemon juice | acid rain | normal rain | pure water | washing-up liquid | pancreatic juice | soap powder | bleach | caustic soda (drain cleaner)

An Indicator is Just a Dye That Changes Colour

The dye in the indicator <u>changes colour</u> depending on whether it's <u>above</u> or <u>below</u> a <u>certain pH</u>. Indicators are very useful for <u>estimating</u> the pH of a solution. There are several different types:

1) <u>Universal indicator</u> is a very useful <u>combination of dyes</u> which gives the colours shown above.

2) <u>Litmus paper</u> tests whether a solution is acidic or alkaline because it changes colour at about pH 7. It's <u>red</u> in <u>acidic</u> solutions, <u>purple</u> in <u>neutral</u> solutions and <u>blue</u> in <u>alkaline</u> solutions.

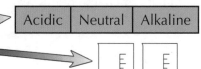

| Acidic | Neutral | Alkaline |

3) <u>Phenolphthalein</u> will change from <u>colourless</u> in <u>acidic</u> solutions to <u>bright pink</u> in <u>alkaline</u> solutions.

4) <u>Methyl orange</u> changes from <u>red</u> in <u>acidic</u> solutions to <u>yellow</u> in <u>alkaline</u> solutions.

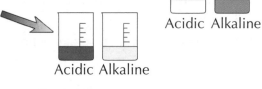

Acidic Alkaline

Acidic Alkaline

Acids can be Neutralised by Bases (or Alkalis)

> An <u>ACID</u> is a source of <u>hydrogen ions</u> (H^+). Acids have a pH of less than 7.
> A <u>BASE</u> is a substance that can neutralise an acid. <u>ALKALIS</u> are <u>soluble bases</u>.
> An alkali is a source of <u>hydroxide ions</u> (OH^-) and has a pH greater than 7.

The reaction between an acid and a base (or an acid and an alkali) is called <u>neutralisation</u>. Make sure you learn it:

$$acid + base \rightarrow salt + water$$

Neutralisation can also be seen in terms of <u>H$^+$</u> and <u>OH$^-$ ions</u> like this, so learn it too:

$$H^+_{(aq)} + OH^-_{(aq)} \rightarrow H_2O_{(l)}$$

When an acid neutralises a base (or vice versa), the <u>products</u> are <u>neutral</u>, i.e. they have a <u>pH of 7</u>.

Reactions of Acids

Acids can react with metals (see page 64), metal oxides and metal carbonates. It seems like there are a lot of reactions on this page, but they all follow a certain pattern — so it's not as tricky as it looks.

Acids react with Metal Oxides to make Salt + Water...

1) Metal oxides are generally bases.

2) This means they'll react with acids to form a salt and water.

> Acid + Metal Oxide → Salt + Water

3) If the acid is hydrochloric acid the salt will be a metal chloride. If it's sulfuric acid the salt will be a metal sulfate. And if it's nitric acid the salt will be a metal nitrate.

For example:

hydrochloric acid + copper oxide → copper chloride + water
$$2HCl + CuO → CuCl_2 + H_2O$$

Copper ion is Cu²⁺, so it needs two Cl⁻ ions.

sulfuric acid + zinc oxide → zinc sulfate + water
$$H_2SO_4 + ZnO → ZnSO_4 + H_2O$$

nitric acid + copper oxide → copper nitrate + water
$$2HNO_3 + CuO → Cu(NO_3)_2 + H_2O$$

✱. { acid + base ⇒ salt + water
acid + metal oxide ⇒ salt + water
acid + metal carbonate ⇒ salt + water + CO₂ }

...and Metal Carbonates to give Salt + Water + Carbon Dioxide

More gripping reactions involving acids. At least there are some bubbles involved here.

> Acid + Metal Carbonate → Salt + Water + Carbon Dioxide

As with metal oxides, the type of salt you get out of the reaction depends on the acid you use. Here are some examples:

hydrochloric acid + sodium carbonate → sodium chloride + water + carbon dioxide
$$2HCl + Na_2CO_3 → 2NaCl + H_2O + CO_2$$

sulfuric acid + calcium carbonate → calcium sulfate + water + carbon dioxide
$$H_2SO_4 + CaCO_3 → CaSO_4 + H_2O + CO_2$$

nitric acid + calcium carbonate → calcium nitrate + water + carbon dioxide
$$2HNO_3 + CaCO_3 → Ca(NO_3)_2 + H_2O + CO_2$$

Don't forget to balance your equations.

Making Salts

Making salts is easy — you just need to know if they're <u>soluble</u> or <u>insoluble</u>...

Salts can be **Soluble** or **Insoluble**

Some salts are soluble (dissolve) in water, others are insoluble (won't dissolve):

- <u>Sodium</u>, <u>potassium</u> and <u>ammonium</u> salts are <u>soluble</u>.
- <u>Nitrates</u> are <u>soluble</u>.
- Most <u>chlorides</u> are <u>soluble</u> — except for silver chloride.
- Most <u>sulfates</u> are <u>soluble</u> — except barium sulfate and calcium sulfate.
- Most <u>carbonates</u> are <u>insoluble</u> — except sodium, potassium and ammonium carbonates.

Making **Soluble Salts** Using **Acids** and **Insoluble Bases**

1) You need to pick the right <u>acid</u>, plus an <u>insoluble base</u> (most <u>metal oxides</u>, <u>metal carbonates</u> and <u>metal hydroxides</u> are insoluble). E.g. if you want to make <u>copper nitrate</u>, mix <u>nitric acid</u> and <u>copper carbonate</u>.

$$CuCO_{3\ (s)} + 2HNO_{3\ (aq)} \longrightarrow Cu(NO_3)_{2\ (aq)} + CO_{2\ (g)} + H_2O_{\ (l)}$$

2) You add the <u>metal oxide</u>, <u>carbonate</u> or <u>hydroxide</u> to the <u>acid</u> — the solid will <u>dissolve</u> in the acid as it reacts. You'll know when all the acid has been neutralised because the excess solid will <u>sink</u> to the bottom of the flask and remain there.

3) You can then <u>filter</u> out the <u>excess</u> base to get the <u>salt solution</u>. To get <u>pure</u>, <u>solid</u> crystals of the <u>salt</u>, <u>evaporate</u> off the water.

filter paper

filter funnel

Making **Soluble Salts** Using an **Alkali**

1) You can't use the method above if you want to neutralise an <u>acid</u> with an <u>alkali</u>. Alkalis are <u>soluble</u> bases so you <u>can't filter them out</u> if you add <u>too much</u> — in fact you can't tell when you've added too much.

2) You have to add <u>exactly</u> the right amount of alkali to <u>just neutralise</u> the acid — you need to use an <u>indicator</u> (see page 96) to show when the reaction's finished. The best way of doing this is to do a <u>titration</u> — see next page. Then <u>repeat</u> using exactly the same volumes of alkali and acid but <u>without an indicator</u> so the salt isn't <u>contaminated</u>.

Making **Insoluble** Salts — **Precipitation** Reactions

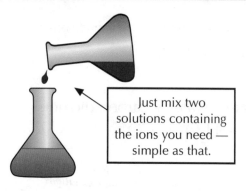

Just mix two solutions containing the ions you need — simple as that.

1) If the salt you want to make is <u>insoluble</u>, you can use a <u>precipitation reaction</u>.

2) You just need to pick <u>two solutions</u> that contain the <u>ions</u> you need. E.g. to make <u>barium sulfate</u> (which is insoluble) you need a solution which contains <u>barium ions</u> and one which contains <u>sulfate ions</u>. So you can mix <u>barium chloride</u> (most chlorides are soluble) with <u>sulfuric acid</u>.

E.g. $BaCl_{2\ (aq)} + H_2SO_{4\ (aq)} \longrightarrow BaSO_{4\ (s)} + 2HCl_{\ (aq)}$

Titrations

Titrations have a bad reputation — but they're not as bad as they're made out to be.

Titrations are Used to Find Out Concentrations

Titrations allow you to find out exactly how much acid is needed to neutralise a quantity of alkali (or vice versa). Here's how you do a titration...

1) Using a pipette and pipette filler, add some alkali (usually about 25 cm³) to a conical flask, along with two or three drops of indicator.
   (The pipette filler stops you getting a mouthful of alkali.)

2) Fill a burette with the acid. Make sure you do this BELOW EYE LEVEL — you don't want to be looking up if some acid spills over.

3) Using the burette, add the acid to the alkali a bit at a time — giving the conical flask a regular swirl. Go especially slowly when you think the end-point (colour change) is about to be reached.

4) The indicator changes colour when all the alkali has been neutralised, e.g. phenolphthalein is pink in alkalis, but colourless in acids.

5) Record the volume of acid used to neutralise the alkali. It's best to repeat this process a few times, making sure you get (pretty much) the same answer each time — this makes for more reliable results.

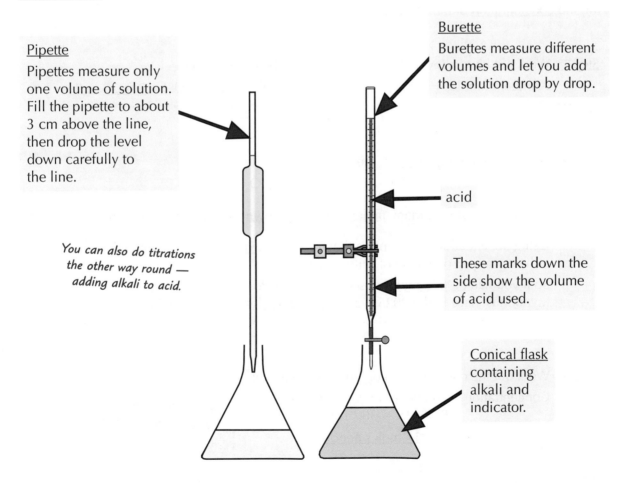

Pipette
Pipettes measure only one volume of solution. Fill the pipette to about 3 cm above the line, then drop the level down carefully to the line.

You can also do titrations the other way round — adding alkali to acid.

Burette
Burettes measure different volumes and let you add the solution drop by drop.

acid

These marks down the side show the volume of acid used.

Conical flask
containing alkali and indicator.

Phenolphthalein is a handy indicator — better learn how to spell it...

The indicator's job is to tell you when the reaction is finished. Phenolphthalein is good for acids and alkalis, but other indicators are possible too. However, don't use universal indicator — it's too hard to tell accurately when the reaction is over. You want an indicator that gives a sudden colour change.

Titrations

Once you've done a titration, you can carry out some <u>calculations</u> with your results.

The **Calculation** — Work Out the **Numbers of Moles**

Basically, you're trying to find the <u>number of moles</u> of each substance (see p. 39).
A <u>formula triangle</u> is pretty handy here, I reckon.

It's the same one as on page 43, conveniently.

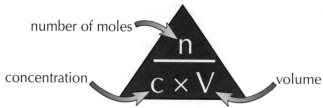

number of moles

concentration

volume

Example:

Suppose you start off with <u>25 cm³</u> of sodium hydroxide solution in your flask, and you know that its concentration is <u>0.1 moles per dm³</u>.
You then find from your titration that it takes <u>30 cm³</u> of sulfuric acid (of an unknown concentration) to neutralise the sodium hydroxide.

Find the <u>concentration</u> of the acid.

<u>Step 1</u>: Work out how many <u>moles</u> of the 'known' substance you have:
Number of moles = concentration × volume = 0.1 × (25 / 1000) = <u>0.0025 moles</u>

<u>Step 2</u>: Write down the <u>equation</u> for the reaction...

$$2NaOH + H_2SO_4 \longrightarrow Na_2SO_4 + 2H_2O$$

...and work out how many <u>moles</u> of the '<u>unknown</u>' stuff you must have had.

Using the equation, you can see that for every <u>two moles</u> of sodium hydroxide you had...
...there was just <u>one mole</u> of sulfuric acid.
So if you had <u>0.0025 moles</u> of sodium hydroxide...
...you must have had 0.0025 ÷ 2 = <u>0.00125 moles</u> of sulfuric acid.

<u>Step 3</u>: Work out the concentration of the '<u>unknown</u>' stuff.
Concentration = number of moles ÷ volume
= 0.00125 ÷ (30 / 1000)
= <u>0.0417 moles per dm³</u>

If you need the concentration in g/dm³, convert your answer using the method on page 43.

Titration calculations really aren't too bad...

Remembering the formula triangle will be a huge help, because you can use that to find the missing values in Step 1 and Step 3. Apart from that, you just need the balanced equation. Easy peasy.

Warm-Up and Exam Questions

It's about time you stopped and checked what you know — have a go at these questions.

Warm-Up Questions

1) What range of values does pH take?
2) What term is used to describe a substance with a pH of 7?
3) Caustic soda is a strong alkali. Suggest what its pH is.
4) Write the word equation for the reaction between sulfuric acid and magnesium oxide.
5) Suggest an indicator that you could use in a titration.

Exam Questions

1   Bleach has a pH of around 12.
Copy and complete the table to show what colour it would turn the following indicators.

Indicator	Colour
Litmus paper	
Phenolphthalein	
Universal indicator	purple
Methyl orange	

(3 marks)

2   A student has a test tube containing some acid. The student adds a few drops of universal indicator to the acid and it turns red. The student then gradually adds some alkali to the test tube.

a)   What type of ions in the acid cause the indicator to become red?

(1 mark)

b)   What type of reaction takes place between the acid and the alkali?

(1 mark)

c)   The student stops adding alkali when all of the acid has reacted.
How will the student know when all of the acid has reacted?

(1 mark)

3   When a sample of calcium carbonate powder is placed in a test tube containing nitric acid, bubbles of gas are given off.

a)   Name the gas evolved during the reaction.

(1 mark)

b)   Write a chemical equation for the reaction.

(2 marks)

c)   Some calcium carbonate powder is left over.
Suggest an appropriate acid that could be added to it to make calcium chloride.

(1 mark)

Exam Questions

4   Precipitation reactions can be used to produce salts.

   a)   Which **two** salt solutions could you mix together to produce the salt calcium sulfate?

   A calcium nitrate   **B** barium sulfate   **C** calcium carbonate   **D** potassium sulfate

(2 marks)

   b)   Describe how you would separate calcium sulfate from the reaction mixture after the reaction has finished.

(1 mark)

5   Copy and complete the following sentences about the solubility of salts, using words from the box below. Each word can be used once, more than once or not at all.

soluble	alkalis	barium	acids	sodium	insoluble

   a)   Most chlorides and nitrates are .... in water.

(1 mark)

   b)   Soluble salts can be made by reacting .... with insoluble bases.

(1 mark)

   c)   Common carbonates are .... in water. Exceptions are

   potassium, ammonium and .... carbonates.

(2 marks)

6   Silver nitrate is a soluble salt. It can be made by adding an excess of insoluble silver carbonate to nitric acid until no further reaction occurs, as shown in the diagram.

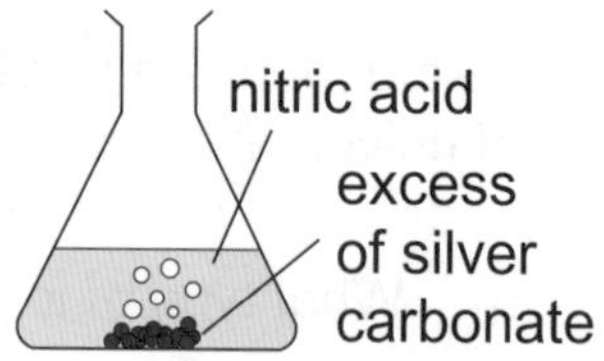

   a)   Give **one** observation that would indicate that the reaction is complete.

(1 mark)

nitric acid

excess of silver carbonate

   b)   Write a word equation for the reaction.

(1 mark)

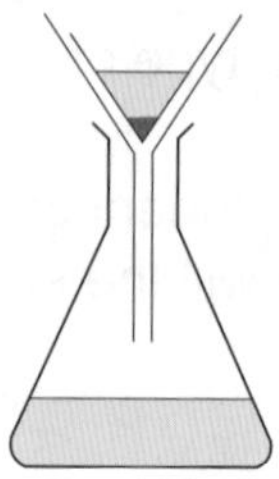

   c)   Once the reaction is complete, the excess silver carbonate can be separated from the silver nitrate solution using the apparatus shown to the right. What is this method of separation called?

(1 mark)

   d)   Describe how you could produce solid silver nitrate from silver nitrate solution.

(1 mark)

   e)   Potassium nitrate can be made by reacting potassium hydroxide with nitric acid.

   i)   Explain why the same method used for making silver nitrate (as above) cannot be used.

(2 marks)

   ii)   Briefly describe how you would produce a solution of pure potassium nitrate from potassium hydroxide and nitric acid.

(3 marks)

Rates of Reaction

Reactions can be <u>fast</u> or <u>slow</u> — you've probably already realised that. This page is about what affects the <u>rate of a reaction</u>, and the next two pages tell you what you can do to <u>measure it</u>.

Reactions Can Go at All Sorts of Different **Rates**

1) One of the <u>slowest</u> is the <u>rusting</u> of iron.
2) A <u>moderate speed</u> reaction is a <u>metal</u> (like magnesium) reacting with <u>acid</u> to produce a gentle stream of <u>bubbles</u>.
3) A <u>really fast</u> reaction is an <u>explosion</u>, where it's all over in a <u>fraction</u> of a second.

The **Rate of a Reaction** Depends on **Four Things**:

1) Temperature
2) Concentration — (or <u>pressure</u> for gases)
3) Catalyst
4) Size of particles — (or surface area)

Typical Graphs for Rate of Reaction

The plot below shows how the speed of a particular reaction varies under <u>different conditions</u>. The quickest reaction is shown by the line that becomes <u>flat</u> in the <u>least</u> time. The line that flattens out first must have the <u>steepest slope</u> compared to all the others, making it possible to spot the slowest and fastest reactions.

1) <u>Graph 1</u> represents the original <u>fairly slow</u> reaction. The graph is not too steep.
2) <u>Graphs 2 and 3</u> represent the reaction taking place <u>quicker</u> but with the <u>same initial amounts</u>. The slope of the graphs gets steeper.
3) The <u>increased rate</u> could be due to <u>any</u> of these:

   1) increase in <u>temperature</u>
   2) increase in <u>concentration</u> (or pressure)
   3) <u>catalyst</u> added
   4) solid reactant crushed up into <u>smaller bits</u> (so it has a bigger surface area).

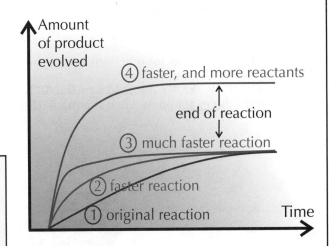

4) <u>Graph 4</u> produces <u>more product</u> as well as going <u>faster</u>. This can <u>only</u> happen if <u>more reactant(s)</u> are added at the start. <u>Graphs 1, 2 and 3</u> all converge at the same level, showing that they all produce the same amount of product, although they take <u>different</u> times to get there.

A steep graph means a speedy reaction

<u>Industrial</u> reactions generally use a <u>catalyst</u> and are done at <u>high temperature and pressure</u>. Time is money, so the faster an industrial reaction goes the better... but only <u>up to a point</u>. Chemical plants are quite expensive to rebuild if they get blown into lots and lots of teeny tiny pieces.

Measuring Rates of Reaction

If you want to know the rate of reaction then it's fairly easy to <u>measure</u> it.
There are <u>three</u> ways of measuring the rate of a reaction on the next two pages...

Three Ways to Measure the *Speed* of a Reaction

The <u>rate of a reaction</u> can be observed <u>either</u> by measuring how quickly the reactants are used up or how quickly the products are formed. It's usually a lot easier to measure <u>products forming</u>.

The rate of reaction can be calculated using the following formula:

$$\text{Rate of reaction} = \frac{\text{amount of reactant used or amount of product formed}}{\text{time}}$$

There are different ways that the rate of a reaction can be <u>measured</u>.
Here's <u>one</u> of them (the other two are on the next page):

1) Precipitation

1) This is when the product of the reaction is a <u>precipitate</u> which <u>clouds</u> the solution.

2) Observe a <u>mark</u> through the solution and measure how long it takes for it to <u>disappear</u>.

3) The <u>quicker</u> the mark disappears, the <u>quicker</u> the reaction.

4) This only works for reactions where the initial solution is rather <u>see-through</u>.

5) The result is very <u>subjective</u> — <u>different people</u> might not agree over the <u>exact</u> point when the mark 'disappears'.

Measuring Rates of Reaction

2) *Change in Mass* (Usually Gas Given Off)

1) Measuring the speed of a reaction that <u>produces a gas</u> can be carried out on a <u>mass balance</u>.

2) As the gas is released the mass <u>disappearing</u> is easily measured on the balance.

3) The <u>quicker</u> the reading on the balance <u>drops</u>, the <u>faster</u> the reaction.

4) When the mass <u>stops changing</u>, the reaction has <u>finished</u>.

5) <u>Rate of reaction graphs</u> are particularly easy to plot using the results from this method.

6) This is the <u>most accurate</u> of these three methods because the mass balance is very accurate. But it has the <u>disadvantage</u> of releasing the gas straight into the room.

3) The **Volume** of Gas Given Off

1) This involves the use of a <u>gas syringe</u> to measure the <u>volume</u> of gas given off.

2) The <u>more</u> gas given off during a given <u>time interval</u>, the <u>faster</u> the reaction.

3) When gas stops being produced, the reaction has <u>finished</u>.

4) A graph of <u>gas volume</u> against <u>time elapsed</u> could be plotted to give a rate of reaction graph.

5) Gas syringes usually give volumes accurate to the <u>nearest millilitre</u>, so they're quite accurate. You have to be quite careful though — if the reaction is too <u>vigorous</u>, you can easily blow the plunger out of the end of the syringe.

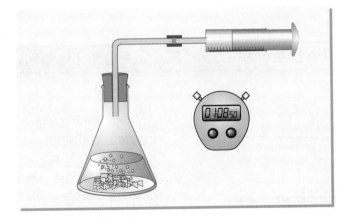

Each of these methods has pros and cons

The mass balance method is only accurate as long as the flask isn't too hot, otherwise you lose mass by <u>evaporation</u> as well as in the reaction. The first method <u>isn't</u> very accurate, but if you're not producing a gas you can't use either of the other two. Ah well.

Rate of Reaction Experiments

Remember: Any reaction can be used to investigate any of the four factors that affect the rate.
The next four pages illustrate four important reactions, but only one factor is considered for each.
But you can just as easily use, say, the marble chips/acid reaction to test the effect of temperature instead.

1) Reaction of Hydrochloric Acid and Marble Chips

This experiment is often used to demonstrate the effect of breaking the solid up into small bits.

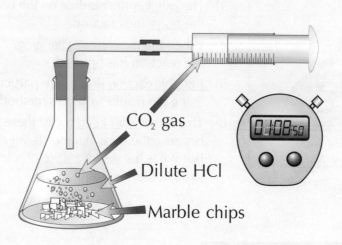

CO₂ gas

Dilute HCl

Marble chips

1) Measure the volume of gas evolved with a gas syringe and take readings at regular intervals.

2) Make a table of readings and plot them as a graph. You choose regular time intervals, so time is the independent variable (x) and volume is the dependent variable (y).

3) Repeat the experiment with exactly the same volume of acid, and exactly the same mass of marble chips, but with the marble more crunched up.

4) Then repeat with the same mass of powdered chalk instead of marble chips.

This Graph Shows the Effect of Using Finer Particles of Solid

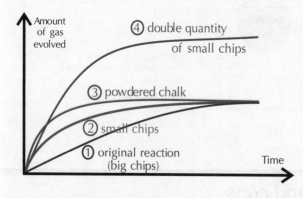

Amount of gas evolved

④ double quantity of small chips

③ powdered chalk

② small chips

① original reaction (big chips)

Time

1) An increase in surface area causes more frequent collisions, so the rate of reaction is faster.

2) Line 4 shows the reaction if a greater mass of small marble chips is added.

3) The extra surface area gives a quicker reaction and there is also more gas evolved overall (as long as the acid is in excess).

Rate of Reaction Experiments

The reaction of <u>magnesium metal</u> with <u>dilute HCl</u> is often used to determine the effect of <u>concentration</u>.

2) Reaction of *Magnesium Metal* With *Dilute HCl*

1) <u>This reaction</u> is good for measuring the effects of <u>increased concentration</u> (as is the marble/acid reaction).

2) This reaction gives off <u>hydrogen gas</u>, which we can measure with a <u>mass balance</u>, as shown.

3) In this experiment, <u>time</u> is again the <u>independent variable</u> and <u>mass loss</u> is the <u>dependent variable</u>.
(The other method is to use a gas syringe, as on the previous page.)

This Graph Shows the Effect of Using *More Concentrated Acid Solutions*

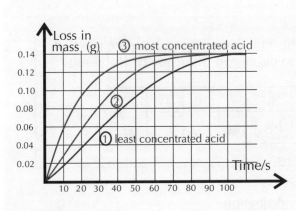

1) Take <u>readings</u> of mass at <u>regular</u> time intervals.

2) Put the results in a <u>table</u> and work out the <u>loss in mass</u> for each reading. <u>Plot a graph</u>.

3) <u>Repeat</u> with <u>more concentrated</u> acid solutions, but always with the <u>same</u> amount of magnesium.

4) The <u>volume</u> of acid must always be kept the <u>same</u> too — only the <u>concentration</u> is increased.

5) The three graphs show the <u>same</u> old pattern — a <u>higher</u> concentration giving a <u>steeper graph</u>, with the reaction <u>finishing</u> much quicker.

Rate of Reaction Experiments

The effect of <u>temperature</u> on the rate of a reaction can be measured using a <u>precipitation</u> reaction.

3) *Sodium Thiosulfate* and *HCl* Produce a *Cloudy Precipitate*

1) These two chemicals are both <u>clear solutions</u>.

2) They react together to form a <u>yellow precipitate</u> of <u>sulfur</u>.

3) The experiment involves watching a black mark <u>disappear</u> through the <u>cloudy sulfur</u> and <u>timing</u> how long it takes to go.

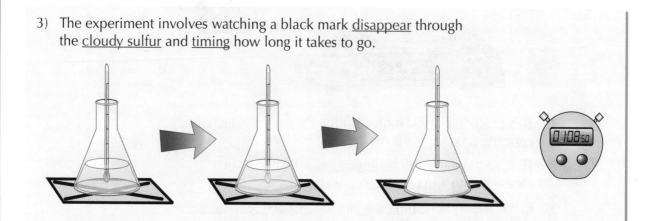

4) The reaction can be <u>repeated</u> for solutions at different <u>temperatures</u>. In practice, that's quite hard to do accurately and safely (it's not a good idea to heat an acid directly). The best way to do it is to use a <u>water bath</u> to heat both solutions to the right temperature <u>before you mix them</u>.

5) The <u>depth</u> of liquid must be kept the <u>same</u> each time, of course.

6) The results will of course show that the <u>higher</u> the temperature the <u>quicker</u> the reaction and therefore the <u>less time</u> it takes for the mark to <u>disappear</u>. These are typical results:

independent variable ⟹	Temperature (°C)	20	25	30	35	40
dependent variable ⟹	Time taken for mark to disappear (s)	193	151	112	87	52

This reaction can <u>also</u> be used to test the effects of <u>concentration</u>.

This reaction <u>doesn't</u> give a set of graphs. All you get is a set of <u>readings</u> of how long it took till the mark disappeared for each temperature.

Rate of Reaction Experiments

Good news — this is the last rate experiment. This one looks at how a <u>catalyst</u> affects rate of reaction.

4) The *Decomposition* of *Hydrogen Peroxide*

This is a <u>good</u> reaction for showing the effect of different <u>catalysts</u>.
The decomposition of hydrogen peroxide is:

$$2H_2O_{2\,(aq)} \quad \rightarrow \quad 2H_2O_{(l)} \quad + \quad O_{2\,(g)}$$

1) This is normally quite <u>slow</u> but a sprinkle of
<u>manganese(IV) oxide catalyst</u> speeds it up no end.
Other catalysts which work are found in:
a) <u>potato peel</u> and b) <u>blood</u>.

2) <u>Oxygen gas</u> is given off, which provides an <u>ideal way</u>
to measure the rate of reaction using the <u>gas syringe</u> method.

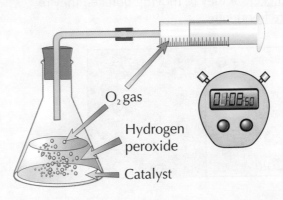

O₂ gas

Hydrogen
peroxide

Catalyst

This Graph Shows the Effect of Using **Different Catalysts**

1) Same old graphs of course.

2) <u>Better</u> catalysts give a <u>quicker reaction</u>,
which is shown by a <u>steeper graph</u> that
levels off quickly.

3) This reaction can also be used to
measure the effects of <u>temperature</u>,
or of <u>concentration</u> of the H_2O_2 solution.
The graphs will look just the same.

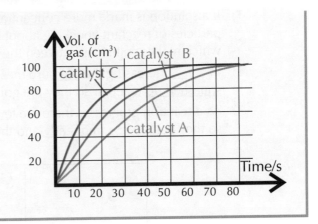

Blood is a catalyst? — eeurgh...

This stuff's about comparing those pretty rate of reaction graphs. They tell you the amount of <u>product</u>
made (or reactant used up) and the <u>rate of reaction</u>. The <u>steeper</u> the curve, the <u>faster</u> the reaction.

Collision Theory

Reaction rates are explained perfectly by <u>collision theory</u>. It's really simple.

1) It just says that <u>the rate of a reaction</u> simply depends on <u>how often</u> and <u>how hard</u> the reacting particles <u>collide</u> with each other.

2) The basic idea is that particles have to <u>collide</u> in order to <u>react</u>, and they have to collide <u>hard enough</u> (with enough energy).

More Collisions Increases the *Rate of Reaction*

All four methods (see below and on the next page) of increasing the <u>rate of reactions</u> can be <u>explained</u> in terms of increasing the <u>number of successful collisions per second</u> between the reacting particles:

1) HIGHER TEMPERATURE

When the <u>temperature is increased</u> the particles have more energy and <u>move quicker</u>. If they're moving quicker, they're going to <u>collide more frequently</u>.

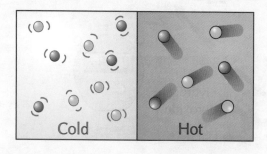

Cold   Hot

2) HIGHER CONCENTRATION (or PRESSURE)

1) If a solution is made more <u>concentrated</u> it means there are more particles of <u>reactant</u> knocking about <u>between the water molecules</u> which makes collisions between the <u>important</u> particles <u>more likely</u>.

2) In a <u>gas</u>, increasing the <u>pressure</u> means the particles are <u>more squashed up</u> together so they are going to <u>collide more frequently</u>.

3) As a reaction progresses there are <u>fewer and fewer reactant particles</u>, so they <u>collide less frequently</u> and the <u>reaction rate slows down</u>.

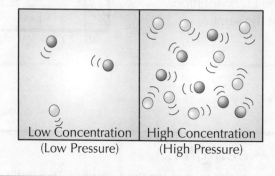

Low Concentration   High Concentration
(Low Pressure)   (High Pressure)

Collision Theory

3) LARGER SURFACE AREA

If one of the reactants is a <u>solid</u> then <u>breaking it up</u> into <u>smaller</u> pieces will <u>increase its surface area</u>. This means the particles around it in the solution will have <u>more area to work on</u>, so there'll be <u>useful collisions more often</u>.

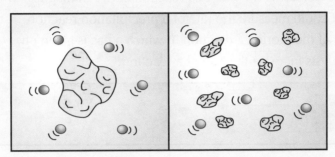

Small surface area   Big surface area

4) CATALYSTS

A <u>solid catalyst</u> works by giving the <u>reacting particles</u> a <u>surface</u> to <u>stick to</u>. They increase the number of <u>SUCCESSFUL</u> collisions by lowering the <u>activation energy</u> (see below and page 116).

Surface of catalyst

Faster Collisions Increase the Rate of Reaction

<u>Higher temperature</u> also increases the <u>energy</u> of the collisions, because it makes all the particles <u>move faster</u>.

<u>Fast collisions</u> are <u>ONLY</u> caused by <u>increasing the temperature</u>.

Reactions <u>only happen</u> if the particles collide with <u>enough energy</u>.

At a <u>higher temperature</u> there will be <u>more particles</u> colliding with <u>enough energy</u> to make the reaction happen — we say there are <u>more successful collisions</u>.

This <u>initial energy</u> is known as the <u>activation energy</u> and it's needed to <u>break the initial bonds</u>.

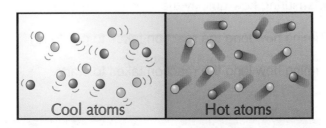

Cool atoms   Hot atoms

Warm-Up and Exam Questions

Try your hand at these questions — it's the best way to see what you've learnt so far.
Read over 'Describing Experiments' on pages 151-154 if you get stuck on the experiments questions.

Warm-Up Questions

1) Give an example of a reaction that happens very slowly, and one that is very fast.
2) Give three ways of increasing the rate of a reaction between magnesium and sulfuric acid.
3) Describe how you could measure the rate of a precipitation reaction.
4) Describe one way of monitoring a reaction in which a gas is given off.
5) How do solid catalysts increase the rate of a reaction?

Exam Questions

1 A teacher demonstrated an experiment to investigate the effect of temperature on rate of reaction. The teacher added dilute hydrochloric acid at 20 °C to marble chips and measured the volume of gas produced at regular time intervals. The teacher then repeated the experiment at 30 °C using the same mass of marble chips of the same size. The results are shown below.

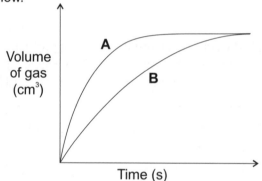

a) Which curve, **A** or **B**, shows the result of the experiment at 30 °C?

(1 mark)

b) Copy the graph and sketch the curve you would expect if you repeated the experiment at 25 °C. Label it **C**.

(1 mark)

c) i) State **one** variable that the teacher would have controlled in order to make the demonstration scientifically valid. Explain why this variable needed to be controlled.

(2 marks)

   ii) Does the graph suggest that the teacher successfully controlled this variable? Explain your answer.

(2 marks)

d) Which other method could be used to measure the rate of this reaction? Chose your answer from one of the methods below.

A Measuring how quickly the reaction loses mass.

B Timing how long the reaction takes to go cloudy.

C Timing how long the reaction takes to start.

(1 mark)

Exam Questions

2 An experiment was set up to compare the rate of reaction of 5 g of magnesium ribbon with 20 ml of five different concentrations of hydrochloric acid. The volume of gas produced during the first minute of the reaction was recorded. The experiment was repeated twice for each concentration of acid. The results obtained are displayed in the table.

Concentration of HCl (mol/dm³)	Experiment 1: volume of gas produced (cm³)	Experiment 2: volume of gas produced (cm³)	Average volume of gas produced (cm³)
2	92	96	
1.5	63	65	
1	44	47	
0.5	20	19	
0.25	9	9	

a) Copy and complete the 'Average volume of gas produced' column.

(2 marks)

b) i) State which concentration of hydrochloric acid produced the fastest rate of reaction.

(1 mark)

ii) Explain your answer to b) i).

(1 mark)

c) The apparatus used in the experiment is shown below.

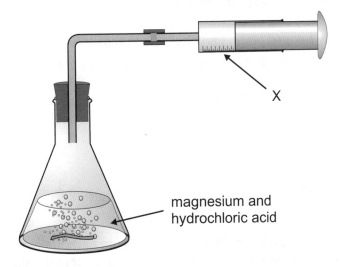

magnesium and hydrochloric acid

X

i) What is the name of the piece of apparatus labelled X?

(1 mark)

ii) Name **one** other piece of apparatus needed for this experiment that is not shown in the diagram.

(1 mark)

d) Why did the student do the experiment twice and calculate the average volume of gas for each concentration of HCl?

(1 mark)

Exam Questions

3   The decomposition of hydrogen peroxide can be used to investigate the effect of a catalyst on the rate of a reaction. Three different catalysts are compared to see which was the most effective (increased the rate of reaction the most). A gas syringe was used to measure the amount of gas produced. Below is a graph of the results.

The three catalysts used in this experiment were potato peel, blood and manganese(IV) oxide. Manganese(IV) oxide is the most effective of these catalysts for this reaction.

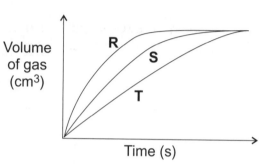

a)   Which curve, **R**, **S** or **T**, represents the reaction using a manganese(IV) oxide catalyst? Explain your answer.

(2 marks)

b)   State **one** variable which must be controlled (kept constant) to ensure the experiment is valid.

(1 mark)

4   Reactions occur when particles collide with each other.

a)   Explain, in terms of collisions, why increasing the pressure of the reactants in a gaseous reaction increases the reaction rate.

(2 marks)

b)   Reactions only happen when particles collide with sufficient energy.

    i)   What is the name given to the minimum amount of energy required?

(1 mark)

    ii)   This energy is more likely to be reached when particles are travelling faster. Suggest how the speed of particles in a reaction could be increased.

(1 mark)

5   Magnesium carbonate is a white solid that reacts with dilute sulfuric acid to form magnesium sulfate, water and carbon dioxide.

A student conducts two experiments using magnesium carbonate and an excess of sulfuric acid. In one experiment the student uses a large chip of magnesium carbonate and in the other the same mass of powdered magnesium carbonate is used.

a)   i)   Which experiment will have the faster reaction rate?

(1 mark)

    ii)   Explain your answer in terms of particle collisions.

(2 marks)

b)   The student decides that the rate of reaction is too high in one of the experiments. The student repeats the experiment using a lower concentration of acid. Explain how this will reduce the reaction rate.

(2 marks)

Energy Transfer in Reactions

In a chemical reaction, <u>energy</u> can be <u>transferred</u> to or from the <u>surroundings</u>, and it's all about making and breaking bonds.

Energy Must Always be **Supplied** to **Break Bonds**

1) During a chemical reaction, <u>old bonds are broken</u> and <u>new bonds are formed</u>.

2) Energy must be <u>supplied</u> to break <u>existing bonds</u> — so bond breaking is an <u>endothermic</u> process.

3) Energy is <u>released</u> when new bonds are <u>formed</u> — so bond formation is an <u>exothermic</u> process.

BOND BREAKING — <u>ENDOTHERMIC</u>   BOND FORMING — <u>EXOTHERMIC</u>

In an **Exothermic** Reaction, Energy is **Given Out**

In an <u>EXOTHERMIC</u> reaction, the energy <u>released</u> in bond formation is <u>greater</u> than the energy used in <u>breaking</u> old bonds.

> An <u>EXOTHERMIC reaction</u> is one which <u>GIVES OUT ENERGY</u> to the surroundings, usually in the form of <u>heat</u> and usually shown by a <u>RISE IN TEMPERATURE</u>.

In an **Endothermic** Reaction, Energy is **Taken In**

In an <u>ENDOTHERMIC</u> reaction, the energy <u>required</u> to break old bonds is <u>greater</u> than the energy <u>released</u> when <u>new bonds</u> are formed.

> An <u>ENDOTHERMIC reaction</u> is one which <u>TAKES IN ENERGY</u> from the surroundings, usually in the form of <u>heat</u> and usually shown by a <u>FALL IN TEMPERATURE</u>.

The **Change in Energy** is Called the **Enthalpy Change**

The <u>overall change</u> in energy in a reaction is called the <u>ENTHALPY change</u>. It has the symbol <u>ΔH</u>.

Δ is the Greek letter 'delta'. It means 'change in'. The H means enthalpy.

1) The units of ΔH are <u>kJ/mol</u> — so it's the amount of energy in kilojoules per mole of reactant.

2) Enthalpy change can have a <u>positive</u> value or a <u>negative</u> value.
    *   If the reaction is <u>exothermic</u>, the value is <u>negative</u> because the reaction is <u>giving out</u> energy.
    *   If the reaction is <u>endothermic</u>, the value is <u>positive</u> because the reaction <u>takes in</u> energy.

Energy Level Diagrams

Remember — chemical reactions involve a change in energy. <u>Energy level diagrams</u> show this change.

Energy Level Diagrams *Show if it's* Exo- *or* Endo-thermic

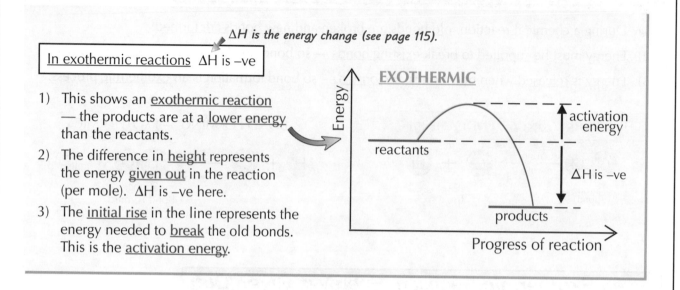

ΔH *is the energy change (see page 115).*

<u>In exothermic reactions</u> ΔH is –ve

1) This shows an <u>exothermic reaction</u> — the products are at a <u>lower energy</u> than the reactants.

2) The difference in <u>height</u> represents the energy <u>given out</u> in the reaction (per mole). ΔH is –ve here.

3) The <u>initial rise</u> in the line represents the energy needed to <u>break</u> the old bonds. This is the <u>activation energy</u>.

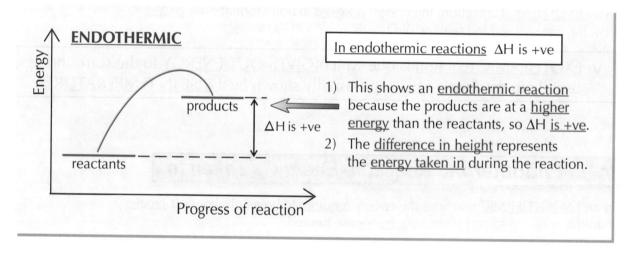

<u>In endothermic reactions</u> ΔH is +ve

1) This shows an <u>endothermic reaction</u> because the products are at a <u>higher energy</u> than the reactants, so ΔH <u>is +ve</u>.

2) The <u>difference in height</u> represents the <u>energy taken in</u> during the reaction.

The Activation Energy *is* Lowered *by* Catalysts

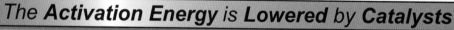

Catalysts are not used up during reactions.

1) The <u>activation energy</u> represents the <u>minimum energy</u> needed by reacting particles for the reaction to occur.

2) A <u>catalyst</u> makes reactions happen <u>faster</u> by providing an <u>alternative reaction pathway</u> (i.e another way for the particles to react) with a <u>lower activation energy</u>.

3) This is represented by the <u>lower curve</u> on the diagram, which shows that <u>less initial energy</u> is needed for the reaction to begin.

4) The <u>overall energy change</u> for the reaction, ΔH, <u>remains the same</u> though.

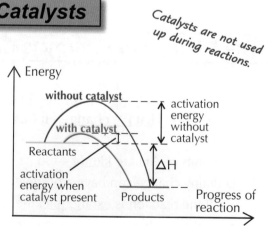

Bond Energy Calculations

You can <u>calculate</u> the <u>enthalpy change</u> for a reaction by looking at the bonds that are made and broken.

Bond Energy — The Amount of Energy in a Bond

1) <u>Each type</u> of chemical bond (e.g. C–C or C–H) has a particular <u>bond energy</u> associated with it.

2) This <u>bond energy</u> can vary slightly depending what <u>compound</u> the bond is in — so you'll be given <u>average bond energies</u> in the exam.

3) You can use these to calculate the <u>enthalpy</u> change for a reaction. The basic idea is really simple — <u>add up</u> the energy of the bonds that are <u>broken</u> and <u>subtract</u> the energy of the bonds that are <u>made</u>.

Example: The Formation of HCl

Using bond energies you can <u>calculate</u> the <u>enthalpy change</u> for this reaction:

$$H_2 + Cl_2 \rightarrow 2HCl$$

The bond energies you need are:
- H–H: +436 kJ/mol
- Cl–Cl: +242 kJ/mol
- H–Cl: +431 kJ/mol

1) <u>BREAKING one mole</u> of H–H and one mole of Cl–Cl bonds <u>requires</u>:

$$436 + 242 = \underline{678 \text{ kJ}}$$

2) <u>FORMING two moles</u> of H–Cl bonds <u>releases</u>:

$$2 \times 431 = \underline{862 \text{ kJ}}$$

3) Then use this formula to calculate the difference:

$$\text{Enthalpy change } (\Delta H) = \frac{\text{Total energy absorbed}}{\text{to break bonds}} - \frac{\text{Total energy released}}{\text{in making bonds}}$$

4) So, $\Delta H = 678 - 862 = \underline{-184 \text{ kJ/mol}}$

5) The ΔH is <u>negative</u>, so the reaction must be <u>exothermic</u>.

You can even draw all this out on an <u>energy level diagram</u>:

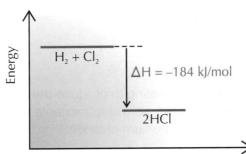

When you're drawing an energy level diagram don't forget to label the reactants, products, ΔH and the axes.

You might get given a slightly <u>more complicated</u> reaction where there are more bonds to break and make, but the method is <u>just the same</u>.

For example in the reaction:

$$CH_4 + 2O_2 \rightarrow CO_2 + 2H_2O$$

There are <u>4 × C–H</u> bonds broken, <u>2 × O=O</u> bonds broken, <u>2 × C=O</u> bonds made and <u>4 × O–H</u> bonds made.

Warm-Up and Exam Questions

You've made it to the next set of questions — see what you've taken in by giving them all a go.

Warm-Up Questions

1) What is an exothermic reaction?
2) What is an endothermic reaction?
3) Is energy released when bonds are formed or when bonds are broken?

Exam Questions

1   During the following reaction, the temperature of the reaction mixture decreases.

$$AB + C \rightarrow AC + B$$

a)   State, with a reason, whether the reaction is exothermic or endothermic.

(2 marks)

b)   Which bond is stronger, **A–B** or **A–C**? Explain your answer.

(2 marks)

c)   i)   What is meant by the **enthalpy change** of a reaction?

(1 mark)

ii)   Is the enthalpy change of the above reaction positive or negative?

(1 mark)

iii) Give the symbol that is used to represent enthalpy change.

(1 mark)

2   Chemical reactions involve enthalpy changes.

a)   The enthalpy change during a reaction is +42 kJ/mol.
     Is the reaction exothermic or endothermic?

(1 mark)

b)   What is meant by the term **activation energy**?

(1 mark)

c)   Explain how catalysts increase the rate of a reaction.

(1 mark)

3   Ammonium chloride is a white solid that decomposes on heating to produce the gases
     ammonia and hydrogen chloride. The reaction is reversible, so when ammonia and
     hydrogen chloride are cooled, they react to form solid ammonium chloride.

$$NH_4Cl_{(s)} \rightleftharpoons NH_{3(g)} + HCl_{(g)}$$

a)   Is the decomposition of ammonium chloride an exothermic or an
     endothermic reaction? Give a reason for your answer.

(2 marks)

b)   In a reversible reaction, the reaction in one direction is exothermic and the
     reaction in the other direction is endothermic. Is the enthalpy change of the
     reaction that forms ammonium chloride positive or negative?

(1 mark)

Exam Questions

4   The diagrams below represent the energy changes in five different chemical reactions.

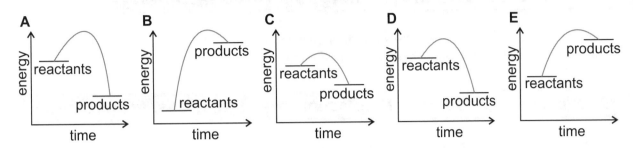

A — energy vs time: reactants, products (lower)
B — energy vs time: products (higher), reactants
C — energy vs time: reactants, products (lower)
D — energy vs time: reactants, products (lower)
E — energy vs time: products (higher), reactants

a)   Choose from the letters **A**, **B**, **C**, **D** or **E** to answer the questions below.
      Each letter may be used once, more than once or not at all. Write the letter of:

    i)   an exothermic reaction.

    ii)   an endothermic reaction.

    iii)   the reaction with the smallest change in energy.

    iv)   the reaction with the largest activation energy.

                                                                               (4 marks)

b)   An energy level diagram is shown below.

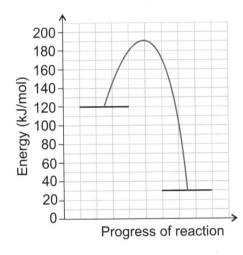

Energy (kJ/mol) vs Progress of reaction. Reactants at 120, peak at ~190, products at ~30.

    i)   Give the enthalpy change for the reaction.
                                                           (1 mark)

    ii)   Give the value of the activation energy.
                                                           (1 mark)

    iii)   Copy the energy level diagram. Sketch the
            curve you would expect if the same reaction
            was repeated in the presence of a catalyst.
                                                           (1 mark)

PAPER 2

5   Calculate the enthalpy change during the combustion of methane.
     The equation for the reaction, displayed formulae of the products and reactants,
     and bond energies are given below.

$$CH_4 + 2O_2 \rightarrow CO_2 + 2H_2O$$

$$\underset{\underset{H}{|}}{\overset{\overset{H}{|}}{H-C-H}} + \begin{matrix} O=O \\ O=O \end{matrix} \longrightarrow O=C=O + \underset{H}{\overset{O}{\diagup}}\underset{H}{} \quad \underset{H}{\overset{O}{\diagup}}\underset{H}{}$$

    C–H = +412 kJ/mol   O=O = +498 kJ/mol   C=O = +743 kJ/mol   O–H = +463 kJ/mol

                                                                               (4 marks)

Measuring Enthalpy Changes

Did you know that you can actually <u>measure</u> all this enthalpy stuff in the lab... oh yes, read on...

You can find out **Enthalpy Changes** using **Calorimetry**

<u>Calorimetry</u> allows you to measure the amount of <u>energy transferred</u> in a <u>chemical reaction</u> with a pretty simple set of equipment. There are two different types of experiment you can do.

Calorimetry — **Dissolving**, **Displacement** and **Neutralisation** Reactions

To measure the amount of <u>energy transferred</u> in these <u>reactions</u> (in solution) you just take the <u>temperature of the reagents</u> (making sure they're the same), <u>mix</u> them and measure the <u>temperature of the solution</u> at the <u>end</u> of the reaction. Easy.

1) So if you want to investigate the enthalpy change of <u>dissolving</u>, <u>displacement</u> (see page 60) or <u>neutralisation</u> reactions (see page 96) you can do it by mixing the reactants in a <u>polystyrene cup</u> (very technical).

2) The biggest <u>problem</u> with energy measurements is the amount of energy <u>lost to the surroundings</u>.

3) You can reduce it a bit by putting the polystyrene cup into a <u>beaker of cotton wool</u> to give <u>more insulation</u>, and putting a <u>lid</u> on the cup to reduce energy lost by <u>evaporation</u>.

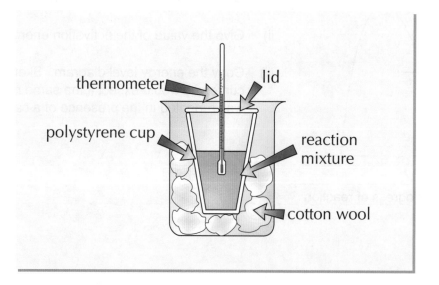

<u>Example:</u>

1) Place 25 cm³ of dilute hydrochloric acid in a polystyrene cup, and record the temperature of the acid.

2) Put 25 cm³ of dilute sodium hydroxide solution in a measuring cylinder and record its temperature.

3) Add the alkali to the acid and stir.

4) Take the temperature of the mixture every 30 seconds, and record the highest temperature it reaches.

Measuring Enthalpy Changes

Here's the other type of experiment you can do...

Calorimetry — *Combustion*

To measure the amount of energy produced when a fuel is burnt, you can simply burn the fuel and use the flame to <u>heat up some water</u>. This method uses a <u>metal container</u>, usually made of <u>copper</u> because copper conducts heat so well.

Method:

1) It's dead important to make as much heat as possible go into <u>heating up</u> the water. <u>Reducing draughts</u> is the key here — use a <u>screen</u> to act as a draught excluder (and don't do it next to an open window).

2) Put 50 g of water in the copper can and <u>record its temperature</u>.

3) <u>Weigh the spirit burner</u> and lid.

4) Put the spirit burner underneath the can, and light the wick. Heat the water, <u>stirring constantly</u>, until the temperature reaches about <u>50 °C</u>.

5) <u>Put out the flame</u> using the burner lid, and measure the <u>final temperature</u> of the water.

6) <u>Weigh</u> the spirit burner and lid <u>again</u>.

7) You can then use the measurements you've taken to <u>calculate the enthalpy change</u> — see the next page.

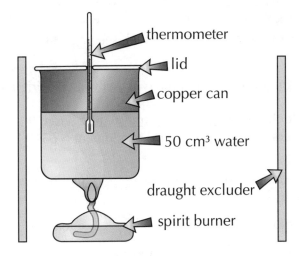

thermometer

lid

copper can

50 cm³ water

draught excluder

spirit burner

Measure the temperature rise to find enthalpy changes...

So you've seen two methods for measuring enthalpy changes. On the next page, you'll see how the results of these experiments can be used in a calculation to work out the heat energy transferred.

Calculating Enthalpy Changes

If you've read the previous pages, you'll know how to get <u>temperature measurements</u> from the start and end of reactions and to work out how much <u>fuel</u> was used for combustion. Now it's calculations time...

Calculate the **Heat Energy Transferred**

1) The <u>combustion</u> experiment on the previous page involves <u>heating water</u> by burning a <u>liquid fuel</u>.

2) If you measure (i) <u>how much fuel</u> you've burned and (ii) the <u>temperature change</u> of the water, you can work out how much energy is supplied by <u>each gram of fuel</u>.

3) You also need to know water's <u>specific heat capacity</u> — this is the <u>amount of energy</u> needed to raise the temperature of <u>1 gram</u> of water by <u>1 °C</u>. The specific heat capacity of <u>water</u> is <u>4.2 J/g/°C</u> — so it takes 4.2 joules of energy to raise the temperature of 1 g of water by 1 °C.

<u>Example: to work out the energy per gram of methylated spirit (meths)</u>:

Mass of spirit burner + lid before heating = 68.75 g
Mass of spirit burner + lid after heating = 67.85 g ⟹ Mass of meths burnt = <u>0.90 g</u>

Temperature of water in copper can before heating = 21.5 °C ⟹ Temperature rise of 50 g of water
Temperature of water in copper can after heating = 52.5 °C due to heating = <u>31.0 °C</u>

So 0.90 g of fuel produces enough energy to heat up 50 g of water by 31 °C.
It takes 4.2 joules of energy to heat up 1 g of water by 1 °C. *You'll be told this in the exam.*
Therefore, the <u>energy produced</u> in this experiment = 4.2 × 50 × 31 = 6510 joules.

So 0.9 g of meths produces 6510 joules of energy...
...meaning 1 g of meths produces 6510/0.9 = <u>7233 J</u> or <u>7.233 kJ</u>.

Energy's wasted heating the can, air, etc. So this figure will often be much lower than the actual energy content.

Calculate the **Molar Enthalpy Change**

Once you've calculated the <u>amount of energy</u> produced you can use it to work out the <u>molar enthalpy change</u> (the enthalpy change given out by one mole of the reactant). See page 39 for more on moles. You need the <u>same info</u> as before and the <u>M_r</u> of the fuel (see page 34).

<u>Example: to work out the energy per mole of methylated spirit (meths)</u>:

1 First, calculate the <u>amount of energy transferred</u>. From the calculation above, we know the energy produced in this experiment = 6510 J or 6.510 kJ.

2 Next, you need to find out <u>how many moles of fuel</u> produced this heat. The M_r of meths is 44.6.

It's back to the old number of moles = $\dfrac{\text{mass (g)}}{M_r}$ equation.

So, number of moles = $\dfrac{0.90}{44.6}$ = 0.020 moles

3 So, the <u>heat produced by 1 mole</u> of fuel = 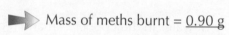 $\dfrac{-6.510}{0.020} \approx -325.5$ kJ/mol

The sign has changed to negative because combustion is an exothermic reaction.

Reversible Reactions

A <u>reversible reaction</u> is one where the <u>products</u> of the reaction can react with each other and <u>convert back</u> to the original reactants. In other words, <u>it can go both ways</u>.

A <u>reversible reaction</u> is one where the <u>products</u> of the reaction can <u>themselves react</u> to produce the <u>original reactants</u>.

$$A + B \rightleftharpoons C + D$$

This is the symbol for a reversible reaction.

The <u>thermal decomposition of ammonium chloride</u> is a reversible reaction: $NH_4Cl_{(s)} \rightleftharpoons NH_{3(g)} + HCl_{(g)}$

1) Ammonium chloride is a <u>white solid</u>. When it's heated it breaks down into the gases <u>ammonia</u> and <u>hydrogen chloride</u> — this is the <u>forward reaction</u>.

2) If you let it cool the <u>ammonia</u> and <u>hydrogen chloride</u> react to <u>re-form</u> the solid — this is the <u>backward reaction</u>.

The <u>dehydration of copper(II) sulfate</u> is another example of a reversible reaction (see page 82).

Reversible Reactions Will Reach **Dynamic Equilibrium**

1) If a reversible reaction takes place in a <u>closed system</u> then a state of <u>equilibrium</u> will always be reached.

2) <u>Equilibrium</u> means that the <u>relative (%) quantities</u> of reactants and products will reach a certain <u>balance</u> and stay there. (A '<u>closed system</u>' just means that none of the reactants or products can <u>escape</u>.)

3) It is in fact a <u>DYNAMIC EQUILIBRIUM</u>, which means that the reactions are still taking place in <u>both directions</u>, but the <u>overall effect is nil</u> because the forward and reverse reactions <u>cancel</u> each other out. The reactions are taking place at <u>exactly the same rate</u> in both directions.

Dynamic Equilibrium

Reactants Combine

Product Splits up

Changing **Temperature** and **Pressure** Can Get You **More Product**

1) In a reversible reaction the 'position of equilibrium' (the relative amounts of reactants and products) depends <u>very strongly</u> on the <u>temperature</u> and <u>pressure</u> of the reacting mixture.

2) If you <u>deliberately alter</u> the temperature and pressure you can <u>move</u> the 'position of equilibrium' to give <u>more product</u> and <u>less</u> reactants.

TEMPERATURE

All reactions are <u>exothermic</u> in one direction and <u>endothermic</u> in the other.
- If you <u>raise</u> the <u>temperature</u>, the <u>endothermic</u> reaction will increase to <u>use up</u> the extra heat.
- If you <u>reduce</u> the <u>temperature</u>, the <u>exothermic</u> reaction will increase to <u>give out</u> more heat.

PRESSURE

Most gaseous reactions have <u>more molecules</u> (or <u>moles</u>) of gas on one side than on the other.
- If you <u>raise</u> the <u>pressure</u> it will encourage the reaction which produces <u>fewer molecules</u> of gas.
- If you <u>lower</u> the <u>pressure</u> it will encourage the reaction which produces <u>more molecules</u> of gas.

Warm-Up and Exam Questions

You've almost reached the end of this section, but don't stop just yet.
Take a look at these questions to make sure you understand everything you've just read.

Warm-Up Questions

1) In a calorimetry experiment involving neutralisation, why should the beaker containing the reagents be insulated?
2) What is meant by the specific heat capacity of water?
3) What does it mean when a reversible reaction reaches equilibrium?
4) What is the effect on an equilibrium of increasing the temperature if the forward reaction is endothermic?
5) What is the effect on an equilibrium of increasing the temperature if the forward reaction is exothermic?
6) For the reaction, $N_{2(g)} + O_{2(g)} \rightleftharpoons 2NO_{(g)}$, what would be the effect on the equilibrium of changing the gas pressure?

Exam Questions

1 A scientist conducted a calorimetry experiment to measure the energy produced when petrol is burnt. 0.7 g of petrol was burned in a spirit burner placed underneath a copper can containing 50 g of water. The temperature of the water increased by 30.5 °C.

a) Why was a copper can chosen to hold the water?

(1 mark)

b) It takes 4.2 J to raise the temperature of 1 g of water by 1 °C.
Calculate the heat energy change in the experiment using the formula:

heat energy change (J) = mass of water (g) × 4.2 × temperature change (°C)

(1 mark)

c) Use your answer to b) to calculate the energy produced per gram of petrol.
Give your answer in kJ/g.

(2 marks)

PAPER 2

2 In a calorimetry experiment, a student found that burning 1.15 g of ethanol raised the temperature of 50 g of water by 34.5 °C.
She calculated that this was a heat energy change of 7245 J.

a) Calculate the number of moles of ethanol that the student burnt in her experiment.

(2 marks)

b) Calculate the molar enthalpy change (in kJ/mol) for the combustion of ethanol.

(2 marks)

Exam Questions

3   In the reaction below, substances A and B react to form substances C and D.

$$2A_{(g)} + B_{(g)} \rightleftharpoons 2C_{(g)} + D_{(g)}$$

a)   What can you deduce about this reaction from the symbol $\rightleftharpoons$?

(1 mark)

b)   What is meant by the term **dynamic equilibrium**?

(2 marks)

c)   In the above reaction, the forward reaction is exothermic.

   i)   Does the reverse reaction take in or give out heat energy?
Explain your answer.

(2 marks)

   ii)   Explain why changing the temperature of a reversible reaction always affects
the position of the equilibrium.

(2 marks)

   iii)   If the temperature of the above reaction is raised, will the equilibrium position
move to the right or to the left?

(1 mark)

d)   State and explain the effect of changing the pressure on the position of equilibrium
in the above reaction.

(2 marks)

e)   Ammonium chloride is heated in a beaker inside a fume cupboard to form ammonia
gas and hydrogen chloride gas. Why can this reaction not reach equilibrium even
though it is reversible?

(1 mark)

4   When blue hydrated copper(II) sulfate is heated, steam
and anhydrous white copper(II) sulfate are produced.

$$CuSO_4.5H_2O_{(s)} \rightleftharpoons CuSO_{4(s)} + 5H_2O_{(g)}$$

a)   From the information given in the question, do you think the forward reaction is
exothermic or endothermic. Give a reason for your answer.

(2 marks)

b)   A student has a beaker containing some anhydrous copper(II) sulfate powder.
A few drops of water are added to the beaker from a pipette.
Two changes are observed in the beaker.

   i)   Describe what happens to the colour of the copper(II) sulfate.

(1 mark)

   ii)   What happens to the temperature of the mixture in the beaker?

(1 mark)

Revision Summary for Section 4

This section is pretty tough. With all the different colours, reactions, methods and calculations, there sure is a lot to remember. If you're feeling overwhelmed by it all, don't be. I've prepared a little something that will help ease you through it — here come the revision summary questions. Go on, have a go.

1) What pH value is given to a neutral solution?

2) What colour does litmus paper go in: a) acidic solutions   b) alkaline solutions?

3) Write out the word equation for the reaction between an acid and a base.

4)* Write out the chemical equation for the reaction between hydrochloric acid and zinc carbonate.

5) Are potassium salts soluble or insoluble?

6) Is silver chloride soluble or insoluble?

7) Name three different pieces of equipment you'd need to carry out a titration and say what you'd use each one for.

8)* Suppose you start off with 25 cm³ of sodium hydroxide solution in a conical flask and its concentration is 0.25 moles per dm³. You find from your titration that it takes 42 cm³ of hydrochloric acid to neutralise the sodium hydroxide. What is the concentration of the acid?

9) Name four things that the rate of a reaction depends on.

10) Describe three different methods of measuring the rate of a reaction.
    Give one advantage and one disadvantage of each method.

11) A student carries out an experiment to measure the effect of surface area on the reaction between marble chips and hydrochloric acid. He measures the amount of gas given off at regular intervals.
    a) Give two factors he must keep constant for it to be a fair test.
    b)* He uses four samples for his experiment:
           Sample A – 10 g of powdered marble,   Sample B – 10 g of small marble chips,
           Sample C – 10 g of large marble chips,   Sample D – 5 g of powdered marble.
       Sketch a graph to show how the amount of gas collected for each sample would change throughout the experiment.

12) Explain how each of the four factors that affect reaction rates increases the number of successful collisions between particles.

13) Draw an energy level diagram for an exothermic reaction.

14) What does a catalyst do to the activation energy of a reaction?
    Show this on your energy level diagram.

15) a)* Calculate the energy change for the following reaction: $2H_2 + O_2 \rightarrow 2H_2O$
        You need these bond energies: H–H: +436 kJ/mol,   O=O: +496 kJ/mol,   O–H: +463 kJ/mol
        Hint: There are 2 O–H bonds in each molecule of water.
    b)* Is this an exothermic or endothermic reaction?

16) The apparatus below is used to measure how much energy is released when pentane is burnt.
    It takes 4.2 joules of energy to heat 1 g of water by 1 °C.
    a)* Using the following data, calculate the amount of energy per gram of pentane.

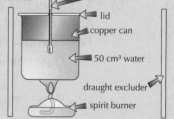

| Mass of empty copper can | 64 g | Initial temperature of water | 17 °C |
| Mass of copper can + water | 116 g | Final temperature of water | 47 °C |

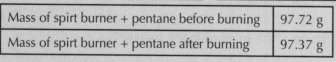

| Mass of spirit burner + pentane before burning | 97.72 g |
| Mass of spirit burner + pentane after burning | 97.37 g |

    b) A data book says that pentane has 49 kJ/g of energy. Why is the amount you calculated different?

17) What is a reversible reaction?

18) How does changing the temperature and pressure of a reversible reaction alter the equilibrium position?

* Answers on page 196.

Metal Ores

Chemistry in industry — time to find out how all those abstract chemical concepts are used in <u>real life</u>. First up — how to get hold of <u>metals</u>. Most metals can't be found as pure lumps. You have to <u>extract</u> them from a <u>compound</u>. And how do you do that, I hear you cry... Funny you should ask...

Most Metals are Found in Ores

1) Metals that are <u>unreactive</u> don't tend to form <u>compounds</u> with other elements. Unreactive metals such as <u>gold</u> are found <u>uncombined</u> — so you just have to find them and dig 'em up.

2) However, most metals <u>do react</u> with other elements to form compounds, which can be found naturally in the <u>Earth's crust</u>.

3) If a compound contains enough of the metal to make it <u>worthwhile extracting</u>, the compound is called a <u>metal ore</u>.

4) There are <u>limited amounts</u> of metal ores — they're "<u>finite resources</u>".

A copper ore

5) The <u>more reactive</u> a metal is, the <u>harder it is to extract it from a compound</u>.

Metals Often have to be **Separated** from their **Oxides**

1) Lots of common metals, like iron and aluminium, react with <u>oxygen</u> to form <u>oxides</u>.

2) These oxides are often the <u>ores</u> that the metals need to be extracted from.

3) A reaction that <u>separates</u> a metal from the oxygen in its oxide is called a <u>reduction reaction</u>.

Example

> In this reaction, copper oxide is <u>reduced</u> to copper.
>
> $$2CuO + C \rightarrow 2Cu + CO_2$$

4) In a reduction reaction, the substance that <u>reduces</u> the metal (and is oxidised) is called the <u>reducing agent</u>.

5) The most common type of reduction reaction uses <u>carbon</u> as a <u>reducing agent</u> to separate the oxygen from the metal.

6) But carbon can't be used for all metals (as you'll see on the next page)...

A loss of oxygen = a reduction reaction

If you need to, have a look back at page 61 to remind yourself about <u>reduction reactions</u>. Getting them clear in your head now will make the next few pages in this section make a lot more sense...

Metal Ores

How easy it is to get a metal out of its ore all comes down to the metal's position in the reactivity series.

Methods of Extraction are Linked to the Order of Reactivity

1) Only metals that are <u>less reactive</u> than <u>carbon</u> can be extracted by a reduction reaction with carbon — this is done by <u>heating</u> the ore with <u>carbon monoxide</u>.

2) This is because <u>more reactive elements</u> form compounds more <u>readily</u>.

3) Carbon's more reactive than iron, so carbon 'steals' oxygen from iron oxide (see page 66). It can also remove oxygen from <u>zinc oxide</u> and <u>tin oxide</u>.

The reduction reaction using carbon is a bit like the displacement reactions with the halogens (see page 60).

4) In other words, carbon <u>can only take the oxygen</u> away from metals which are <u>less reactive</u> than carbon <u>itself</u> is.

5) Very reactive metals form very <u>stable</u> ores — i.e. it's difficult to get the metal out of its compound.

6) So metals that are <u>more reactive</u> than carbon (they come <u>higher</u> in the <u>reactivity series</u>) have to be extracted using <u>electrolysis</u>.

7) Electrolysis uses <u>electricity</u> to <u>separate the metal</u> from the other elements in the compound (see next page).

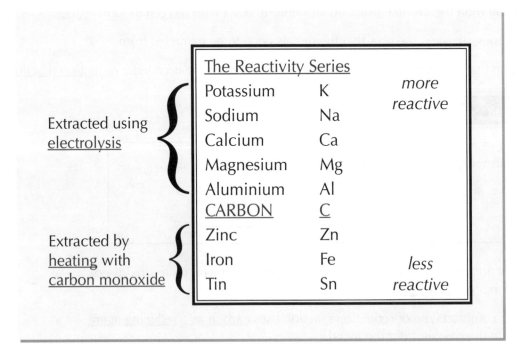

Extracted using <u>electrolysis</u>

Extracted by <u>heating</u> with <u>carbon monoxide</u>

The Reactivity Series		
Potassium	K	*more reactive*
Sodium	Na	
Calcium	Ca	
Magnesium	Mg	
Aluminium	Al	
<u>CARBON</u>	<u>C</u>	
Zinc	Zn	
Iron	Fe	*less reactive*
Tin	Sn	

You can work out the reactivity of a metal...

Experiments can tell you where elements are in the <u>reactivity series</u>. If you can extract a metal from its oxide by reacting it with carbon, then you know that the metal is <u>less reactive</u> than carbon. Simple.

Extracting Aluminium

As aluminium's more reactive than carbon, it has to be extracted from its ore using electrolysis...

Electrolysis Removes Aluminium from Its Ore

1) Aluminium's a very abundant metal, but it is always found naturally in compounds.
2) The main ore is bauxite, and after mining and purifying, a white powder is left.
3) This is pure aluminium oxide, Al_2O_3.

Cryolite is Used to Lower the Temperature (and Costs)

1) Al_2O_3 has a very high melting point of over 2000 °C — so melting it would be very expensive.
2) Instead the aluminium oxide is dissolved in molten cryolite (a less common ore of aluminium).
3) This brings the temperature down to about 900 °C, which makes it much cheaper and easier.
4) The electrodes are made of graphite, a good conductor of electricity.

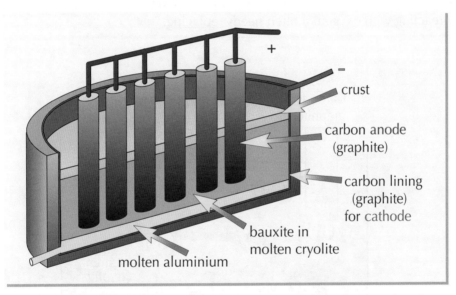

The process of using electrolysis to remove aluminium from its molten ore is covered on the next page.

Electrolysis is Expensive — It's All That Electricity...

1) Electrolysis uses a lot of electricity and that can make it pretty expensive.
2) Energy is also needed to heat the electrolyte mixture to 900 °C. This is expensive too.
3) The positive electrodes need frequent replacement. That costs money as well.
4) But in the end, aluminium now comes out as a reasonably cheap and widely-used metal. A hundred years ago it was a very rare metal, simply because it was so hard to extract.

Cost vs. benefit...

Electrolysis isn't cheap, but it's pretty useful when it comes to getting hold of metals. Make sure you understand why electrolysis is so expensive and why cryolite is used in the electrolysis of Al_2O_3.

Extracting Aluminium

Yes, it's the bit you've been waiting for... time to find out what actually happens at those electrodes...

Electrolysis — Turning **Ions** into the **Atoms** You Want

1) Molten aluminium oxide contains free ions — so it'll conduct electricity.

2) The positive Al^{3+} ions are attracted to the negative electrode (cathode) where they pick up electrons and "zup", they turn into aluminium atoms. These then sink to the bottom.

3) The negative O^{2-} ions are attracted to the positive electrode (anode) where they lose electrons. The oxygen atoms will then react together to form O_2, or with the carbon anode as well to form CO_2.

4) As the positive carbon electrode is constantly getting worn down by reacting with oxygen, it often needs replacing.

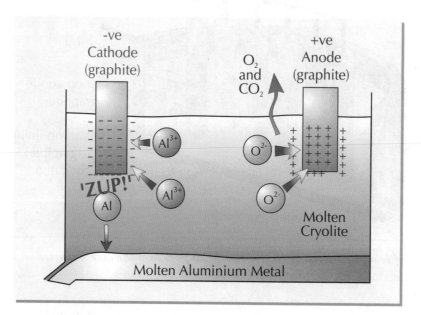

Overall, this is a REDOX reaction (reduction and oxidation both take place). You need to know the reactions at both electrodes:

At the negative electrode (cathode):
$$Al^{3+} + 3e^- \rightarrow Al$$
(Reduction — a gain of electrons)

At the positive electrode (anode):
$$2O^{2-} \rightarrow O_2 + 4e^-$$
(Oxidation — a loss of electrons)

The complete equation for the decomposition of aluminium oxide is then:

There's loads more on half-equations and electrolysis on pages 48-52.

> **aluminium oxide → aluminium + oxygen**

Extracting Iron

Iron is extracted from <u>haematite</u>, Fe_2O_3, by <u>reduction</u> (i.e. removal of oxygen) in a blast furnace.

The Raw Materials are **Iron Ore**, **Coke** and **Limestone**

1) The <u>iron ore</u> contains the <u>iron</u> — which is pretty important.
2) The <u>coke</u> is almost <u>pure carbon</u>. This is for <u>reducing</u> the <u>iron oxide</u> to <u>iron metal</u>.
3) The <u>limestone</u> takes away <u>impurities</u> in the form of <u>slag</u>.

Reducing the **Iron Ore** to **Iron**:

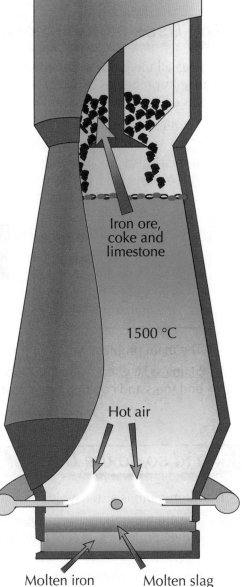

Iron ore, coke and limestone

1500 °C

Hot air

Molten iron   Molten slag

1) <u>Hot air</u> is blasted into the furnace, making the coke <u>burn much faster</u> than normal. This raises the <u>temperature</u> to about <u>1500 °C</u>.

2) The <u>coke burns</u> and produces <u>carbon dioxide</u>:

$$C + O_2 \rightarrow CO_2$$

carbon + oxygen → carbon dioxide

3) The <u>CO_2</u> then reacts with <u>unburnt coke</u> to form <u>CO</u>:

$$CO_2 + C \rightarrow 2CO$$

carbon dioxide + carbon → carbon monoxide

4) The <u>carbon monoxide</u> then <u>reduces</u> the <u>iron ore</u> to <u>iron</u>:

$$3CO + Fe_2O_3 \rightarrow 3CO_2 + 2Fe$$

carbon monoxide + iron(III) oxide → carbon dioxide + iron

5) The <u>iron</u> is <u>molten</u> at this temperature and it's also very <u>dense</u>, so it runs straight to the <u>bottom</u> of the furnace where it's <u>tapped off</u>.

Removing the **Impurities**:

1) The <u>main impurity</u> is <u>sand</u> (silicon dioxide). This is still <u>solid</u>, even at 1500 °C, and would tend to stay mixed in with the iron. <u>The limestone removes it</u>.

2) The limestone is <u>decomposed</u> by the heat into <u>calcium oxide</u> and <u>CO_2</u>.

$$CaCO_3 \rightarrow CaO + CO_2$$

3) The <u>calcium oxide</u> then reacts with the <u>sand</u> to form <u>calcium silicate</u>, or <u>slag</u>, which is molten and can be tapped off:

$$CaO + SiO_2 \rightarrow CaSiO_3 \text{ (molten slag)}$$

4) The cooled slag is <u>solid</u>, and is used for:
 • <u>Road-building</u>   • <u>Fertiliser</u>

Uses of Iron and Aluminium

Iron and aluminium are the most produced metals in the world, so you need to know lots about them...

Iron and Aluminium have some Properties in Common

Both iron and aluminium have the same basic properties — they are both metals after all.

1) They are both dense and lustrous (i.e. shiny).
2) They have high melting points — iron melts at 1538 °C and aluminium melts at 660 °C.
3) They both have a high tensile strength — they're strong and hard to break.
4) But they can also be hammered into a different shape (they're malleable).
5) They are both good conductors of electricity...
6) ...and of heat energy too.

There's more on the properties of metals on page 47.

The Uses of Iron Depend on Its Properties...

Iron has all the properties you'd expect a metal to have. Adding other materials to the iron can change its properties though. This makes it really useful — different properties make it suitable for lots of different uses.

1) Wrought iron is almost completely pure iron. It's malleable, so it's used to make ornamental gates and railings.

2) You can also mix iron with other elements to make alloys. These alloys have different properties to pure iron. For example:

- Cast iron is a mixture of iron, carbon and silicon. It's very hard, but brittle. Cast iron is used for manhole covers and some cooking pans.
- Steel is an alloy made of iron, carbon and (usually) some other metals. Steel has more useful properties than iron — e.g. it's harder than pure iron, but can still be hammered easily into sheets and welded together. These properties mean that steel is great for making car bodies and girders (for construction).

---

3) The main problem with iron is that it corrodes easily (i.e. it rusts).
4) Stainless steel is an alloy made of iron and chromium that doesn't rust. It's used for knives and forks and cooking pans. Makes sense — eating from a rusty fork doesn't really appeal...

...and so do the Uses of Aluminium

1) Aluminium is also a typical metal. However, unlike iron, it doesn't corrode easily.
2) The aluminium reacts very quickly with oxygen in the air to form aluminium oxide. A nice protective layer of aluminium oxide sticks firmly to the aluminium below and stops any further reaction taking place.
3) Because aluminium doesn't corrode it's useful for products that come in contact with water, e.g. drinks cans — you wouldn't want rust in your fizzy pop.
4) Aluminium is also much less dense than iron, which makes it lighter.
5) This makes it useful when the weight of the metal is important, e.g. in bicycle frames and aeroplanes.

Warm-Up and Exam Questions

Brace yourself — it's time to see what you've learnt...

Warm-Up Questions

1) How do you extract a metal that is less reactive than carbon from its ore?
2) What is Al_2O_3?
3) Name the ore that iron is usually extracted from.
4) What is slag? How is it produced in a blast furnace?

Exam Questions

1 Not all metals can be extracted using carbon.
  Some need to be extracted using a different method.

  a) Give the name of the process used to extract these metals.

  (1 mark)

  b) Explain why not all metals can be extracted using carbon.

  (1 mark)

2 Aluminium is extracted from purified aluminium oxide by electrolysis.

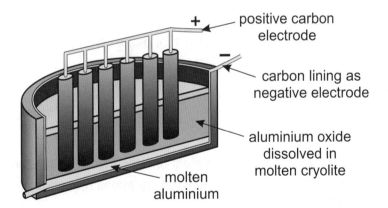

+ positive carbon electrode

– carbon lining as negative electrode

aluminium oxide dissolved in molten cryolite

molten aluminium

  a) Electrolysis is an expensive process.

  i) What makes this process so expensive?

  (1 mark)

  ii) How does dissolving aluminium oxide in cryolite help reduce the cost of electrolysis?

  (2 marks)

  b) A different reaction occurs at each electrode in the electrolysis of aluminium oxide.
  Give the two ionic half-equations that represent these reactions.

  (3 marks)

  c) Are aluminium ions oxidised or reduced in this electrolysis reaction?
  Explain your answer.

  (2 marks)

  d) Another cost associated with the electrolysis of aluminium ore is the replacement
  of electrodes. Which electrode needs to be regularly replaced? Explain why.

  (2 marks)

Exam Questions

3   Iron and aluminium have similar properties. For example, they both have high melting points.
   a)   State **three** other properties that iron and aluminium have in common.

   (3 marks)

   b)   Aluminium is used in the manufacture of aeroplanes.
        Suggest why aluminium is more suited to this role than iron.

   (1 mark)

4   The properties of iron are changed when it is converted into an alloy.
   The table below contains information about two different alloys of iron — cast iron and steel.

Alloy	Hardness	Malleability
Cast iron	Very hard	Poor
Steel	Very hard	Very good

   a)   Suggest which of these alloys is used for the construction of car bodies.
        Give a reason for your choice.

   (2 marks)

   b)   Stainless steel is an alloy that is often used to make knives, forks and other kitchen
        equipment. Suggest a property of this alloy that makes it well suited for this use.

   (1 mark)

5   The main stages of the extraction of iron in a blast furnace involve converting iron ore to iron.
   a)   i)   Copy and complete the following chemical equations that show the first two
             steps in the process.

             Step 1:   C   + ...   →   ....

             Step 2:   ....   + ...   →   2CO

   (2 marks)

        ii)   Describe what happens in the blast furnace when these reactions occur.

   (2 marks)

   b)   i)   Write a balanced chemical equation to show the production of iron from iron ore
             using carbon monoxide.

   (2 marks)

        ii)   In this reaction is the iron oxide reduced or oxidised?

   (1 mark)

Fractional Distillation of Crude Oil

Crude Oil is Separated into Different Hydrocarbon Fractions

Crude oil is a <u>mixture</u> of substances, most of which are <u>hydrocarbons</u> — molecules which are made of just carbon and hydrogen. The different compounds in crude oil are <u>separated</u> by <u>fractional distillation</u>:

1) The oil is <u>heated</u> until most of it has turned into <u>gas</u>.

2) The gases enter a <u>fractionating column</u> (and the liquid bit, <u>bitumen</u>, is <u>drained off</u> at the bottom).

3) In the column there's a <u>temperature gradient</u> (i.e. it's <u>hot</u> at the <u>bottom</u> and gets gradually <u>cooler</u> as you go up). When the substances that make up crude oil reach a part of the column where the temperature is <u>lower</u> than their boiling point they <u>condense</u> (turn back into a liquid).

4) The <u>longer hydrocarbons</u> have <u>high boiling points</u>. They <u>condense</u> and <u>drain out</u> of the column <u>early on</u>, when they're near the <u>bottom</u>.

5) The <u>shorter</u> hydrocarbons have <u>lower boiling points</u>. They turn to liquid and drain out much <u>later on</u>, near to the <u>top</u> of the column where it's cooler.

6) <u>Bubble caps</u> in the fractionating column stop the separated liquids from running back down the column and <u>remixing</u>.

7) You end up with the crude oil mixture separated out into <u>different fractions</u>. Each fraction contains a mixture of hydrocarbons with <u>similar boiling points</u>.

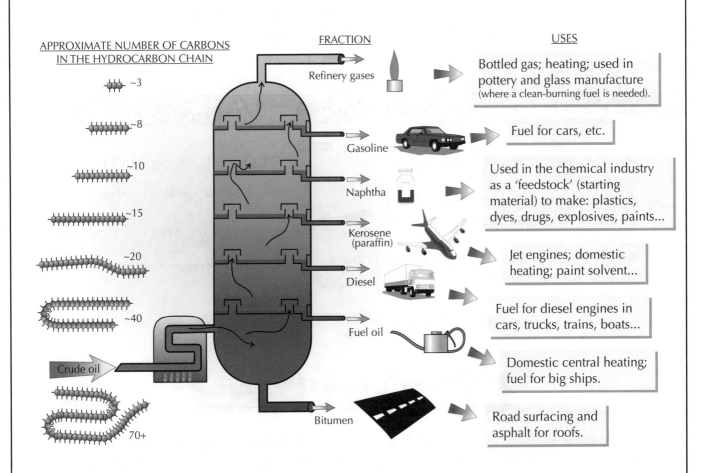

APPROXIMATE NUMBER OF CARBONS IN THE HYDROCARBON CHAIN

~3
~8
~10
~15
~20
~40
70+

Crude oil

FRACTION

Refinery gases

Gasoline

Naphtha

Kerosene (paraffin)

Diesel

Fuel oil

Bitumen

USES

Bottled gas; heating; used in pottery and glass manufacture (where a clean-burning fuel is needed).

Fuel for cars, etc.

Used in the chemical industry as a 'feedstock' (starting material) to make: plastics, dyes, drugs, explosives, paints...

Jet engines; domestic heating; paint solvent...

Fuel for diesel engines in cars, trucks, trains, boats...

Domestic central heating; fuel for big ships.

Road surfacing and asphalt for roofs.

Fractional distillation is an example of a <u>physical process</u> — there are <u>no chemical reactions</u>.

Pollutants

You don't have to be studying for a qualification in chemistry to know that <u>burning fuel</u> can produce <u>pollution</u>. But seeing as you <u>are</u> studying for a qualification in chemistry you'd best learn the <u>details</u>...

Burning Fuels Can Produce Pollutants

A lot of the fractions obtained from crude oil are burnt as <u>fuels</u>. When they're burnt, <u>pollutants</u> such as <u>carbon monoxide</u>, <u>nitrogen oxides</u> and <u>sulfur dioxide</u> may be produced...

Carbon Monoxide is Produced by Incomplete Combustion

1) <u>Carbon monoxide</u> (CO) is formed when hydrocarbon fuels (e.g. <u>petrol</u> or <u>diesel</u> in car engines, or <u>gas</u> in central heating) are burnt without enough oxygen — this is <u>incomplete combustion</u> (see page 88).

2) <u>Carbon monoxide</u> is <u>poisonous</u> — it can stop your blood cells doing their proper job of <u>carrying oxygen</u> around the body. It combines with <u>haemoglobin</u> in blood cells, meaning the blood can carry <u>less oxygen</u>.

3) A lack of oxygen in the blood can lead to <u>fainting</u>, a <u>coma</u> or even <u>death</u>.

Sulfur Dioxide and Nitrogen Oxides Come from Burning Fuel

1) <u>Sulfur dioxide</u> (SO_2) and <u>nitrogen oxides</u> are also released when fossil fuels are burnt.

2) The <u>sulfur dioxide</u> comes from <u>sulfur impurities</u> in the <u>fossil fuels</u>.

3) <u>Nitrogen oxides</u> are created when the temperature is <u>high</u> enough for the nitrogen and oxygen <u>in the air</u> to react. This often happens in car engines. Nitrogen oxides include <u>nitrogen monoxide</u> (NO) and <u>nitrogen dioxide</u> (NO_2).

Acid Rain is Caused by Sulfur Dioxide and Nitrogen Oxides

1) All rain is <u>slightly acidic</u> because <u>carbon dioxide</u> in the air reacts with water to produce a slightly acidic solution.

$$CO_{2(g)} + H_2O_{(l)} \rightarrow H_2CO_{3(aq)}$$

carbon dioxide + water → carbonic acid

2) But when <u>sulfur dioxide</u> mixes with <u>clouds</u> it forms dilute <u>sulfuric acid</u>, which is much more acidic.

3) <u>Nitrogen oxides</u> can also form <u>nitric acid</u> in clouds.

$$2SO_{2(g)} + O_{2(g)} + 2H_2O_{(l)} \rightarrow 2H_2SO_{4(aq)}$$

sulfur dioxide + oxygen + water → sulfuric acid

4) The rain that falls from these clouds is called <u>acid rain</u>.

5) <u>Acid rain</u> causes <u>lakes</u> to become <u>acidic</u> and many plants and animals <u>die</u> as a result.

6) Acid rain kills <u>trees</u> and damages <u>limestone buildings</u> and ruins <u>stone statues</u>. It's shocking.

7) Links between acid rain and human health problems have been suggested.

Cracking Hydrocarbons

The really long hydrocarbons aren't all that useful — but it's OK 'cause they can be made smaller...

Cracking — *Splitting Up* Long-Chain Hydrocarbons

1) <u>Long</u> hydrocarbons have <u>high</u> boiling points and are <u>viscous</u> (thick and gloopy).

2) <u>Shorter</u> hydrocarbons have <u>lower</u> boiling points and are much <u>thinner</u> and <u>paler</u> in colour.

3) Demand for <u>short-chain</u> hydrocarbons like octane, which is used in petrol, is much <u>higher</u> than for longer-chain hydrocarbons.

4) So, to <u>meet</u> this demand, long-chain hydrocarbons are <u>split</u> into <u>more useful</u> short-chain molecules using <u>cracking</u>.

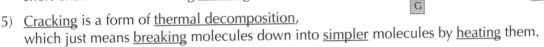

5) <u>Cracking</u> is a form of <u>thermal decomposition</u>, which just means <u>breaking</u> molecules down into <u>simpler</u> molecules by <u>heating</u> them.

6) Cracking also produces <u>alkenes</u>, which are used to make <u>polymers</u> (see next page).

Conditions for Cracking: **Heat**, Plus a **Catalyst**

In industry, <u>vaporised hydrocarbons</u> are passed over a <u>powdered catalyst</u> at about <u>600 °C – 700 °C</u>. <u>Silica</u> (SiO_2) and <u>alumina</u> (Al_2O_3) are used as <u>catalysts</u>.
You can carry out the reaction in the lab using simple equipment. Like this...

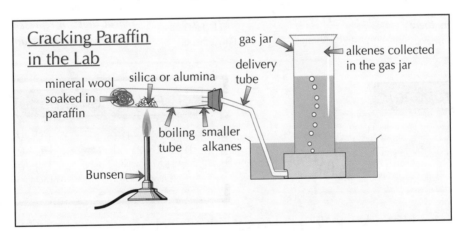

1) Start by <u>heating</u> the <u>paraffin</u>. After a few seconds, <u>move</u> the Bunsen burner to heat the <u>silica</u> or <u>alumina catalyst</u>. <u>Alternate</u> between the two until the paraffin <u>vaporises</u> and the catalyst <u>glows red</u>.

2) The heated paraffin vapour <u>cracks</u> as it passes over the heated catalyst.

3) <u>Small alkanes</u> collect at the end of the boiling tube, while <u>alkene gases</u> travel down the delivery tube.

4) The alkenes are then collected through <u>water</u> using a <u>gas jar</u>.

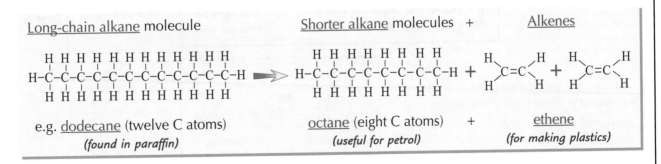

Addition Polymers

Plastics are formed when lots of small molecules called <u>monomers</u> join together to make a <u>polymer</u>. There are two basic types of polymer — <u>addition</u> (see below) and <u>condensation</u> (see next page).

Addition Polymers are Made Under **High Pressure**

The monomers that make up addition polymers have a <u>carbon-carbon double bond</u> — they're <u>alkenes</u> (see pages 89 and 90).

Under <u>high pressure</u> and with a <u>catalyst</u> to help them along, many <u>small molecules</u> will open up those <u>double bonds</u> and 'join hands' (polymerise) to form <u>very long saturated chains</u> — polymers. <u>Ethene</u> becoming <u>poly(ethene)</u> is the easiest example:

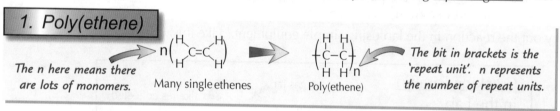

Polymers can be Shown Using **Repeating Units**

Addition polymerisation reactions can be written as an equation using <u>repeating units</u>. For example:

1. Poly(ethene)

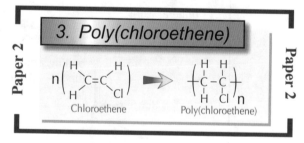

The n here means there are lots of monomers.   Many single ethenes   Poly(ethene)   *The bit in brackets is the 'repeat unit'. n represents the number of repeat units.*

2. Poly(propene)

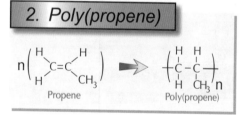

Propene   Poly(propene)

Paper 2

3. Poly(chloroethene)

$$n \left(\begin{array}{c} H \\ C=C \\ H \end{array} \begin{array}{c} H \\ \\ Cl \end{array} \right) \rightarrow \left(\begin{array}{c} H \ H \\ C-C \\ H \ Cl \end{array} \right)_n$$

Chloroethene   Poly(chloroethene)

Paper 2

In the exam, you could be asked to <u>draw the repeat unit</u> of a polymer. You just have to find the section of polymer that's repeated and draw it out. For example:

$$\begin{array}{c} H \ CH_3 \ H \ CH_3 \ H \ CH_3 \\ -C-C-C-C-C-C- \\ H \ H \ H \ H \ H \ H \end{array} \Rightarrow \begin{array}{c} H \ CH_3 \\ -C-C- \\ H \ H \end{array}$$

This section of the polymer is repeated over and over again...   *...so it must be the repeat unit.*

The name of the polymer comes from the monomer it's made from — you just put brackets around the monomer and stick the word 'poly' in front of it.

To find the <u>monomer</u> used to form an addition polymer, take the repeat unit and <u>add a double bond</u>.

$$\begin{array}{c} H \ CH_3 \\ -C-C- \\ H \ H \end{array} \Rightarrow \begin{array}{c} H \ \ \ \ CH_3 \\ C=C \\ H \ \ \ \ H \end{array}$$

Repeat unit   Monomer

More on Polymers and Their Uses

Yep, more on <u>polymers</u>. Well, it's such a <u>great</u> topic, you wouldn't want just <u>one page</u> on it would you...

Polymers can be Made by Condensation Polymerisation

1) <u>Condensation polymerisation</u> usually involves <u>two different types</u> of monomer.
2) The monomers react together and <u>bonds</u> form between them, making polymer chains.
3) For <u>each new bond</u> that forms, a <u>small molecule</u> (for example, water) is <u>lost</u>.
4) <u>Nylon</u> is an example of a condensation polymer.

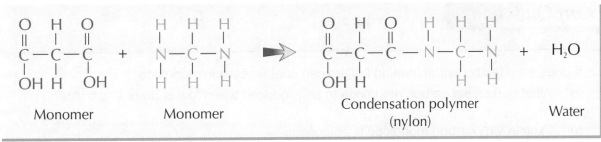

Monomer   Monomer   Condensation polymer (nylon)   Water

Polymers Have Lots of Uses

Different polymers have different <u>physical properties</u>, which makes them suitable for various <u>different uses</u>. For example:

1) <u>Poly(ethene)</u> is a light, stretchable polymer. This makes it ideal for making <u>packaging</u> such as <u>plastic bags</u>, <u>bottles</u> and other <u>containers</u>.
2) <u>Poly(propene)</u> is a very tough polymer, but it's relatively flexible and resistant to heat. It's used to make things like <u>kettles</u>, <u>food containers</u> and <u>carpets</u>.

——— Paper 2 ———
3) <u>Poly(chloroethene)</u> is used to makes <u>clothes</u> and <u>pipes</u> and for <u>insulating electrical cables</u>.
——— Paper 2 ———

Most Polymers are Hard to Get Rid Of

1) Most <u>addition polymers</u> are <u>inert</u> — they don't react easily. This is because the <u>carbon-carbon bonds</u> in the polymer chain are very <u>strong</u> and aren't easily broken.
2) This means that it takes a really long time for addition polymers to <u>biodegrade</u> (be broken down by bacteria or other organisms) — if you bury them in a landfill site, they'll <u>still</u> be there <u>years later</u>.
3) <u>Burning</u> plastics can release <u>toxic gases</u>, so that's not a great idea either.
4) So it's difficult to dispose of polymers. The best thing is to <u>reuse</u> them as many times as possible and then <u>recycle</u> them if you can.

Make sure you know your polymers...

Addition polymers are formed when identical monomers are joined together. Condensation polymers are made when different monomers react together. The only product of addition polymerisation is the polymer, but condensation polymerisation also produces another small molecule. Phew.

Warm-Up and Exam Questions

Lots of tricky stuff in this section. Let's see if you know your pollutants from your polymers...

Warm-Up Questions

1) What is the temperature range used for cracking in industry?
2) How are addition polymers made?
3) State one use of poly(ethene).

Exam Questions

1   Fumes from faulty central heating boilers can contain carbon monoxide.
    a)   What can cause carbon monoxide to be produced when fuel is burnt in a boiler?
(1 mark)

    b)   Explain why carbon monoxide is poisonous.
(1 mark)

2   Cracking alters the molecules obtained in fractional distillation.
    a)   Why is cracking necessary?
(4 marks)

    b)   The apparatus to the right can be used to crack paraffin in the lab.

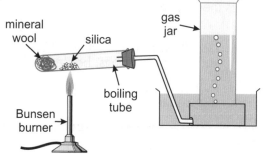

        i)   Identify where the paraffin
              is within the apparatus.
(1 mark)

        ii)   What is the role of silica?
(1 mark)

        iii) What collects in the gas jar?
(1 mark)

3   Nitrogen oxides can be produced when fossil fuels are burnt.
    a)   i)   Describe the conditions needed for nitrogen oxides to form.
(1 mark)

        ii)   Give an example of where this reaction might take place.
(1 mark)

    b)   Nitrogen oxides react with moisture in the atmosphere.
         Name the product that is formed when this occurs.
(1 mark)

    c)   Nitrogen oxides contribute to acid rain.
        i)   Name one other gas that contributes to acid rain.
(1 mark)

        ii)   Give **two** effects of acid rain on the environment.
(2 marks)

4   Most addition polymers are difficult to dispose of, so it's good
    for the environment to reuse them as many times as possible.
    Explain why addition polymers are difficult to dispose of.
(2 marks)

Exam Questions

5 Crude oil can be separated by fractional distillation into several different fractions.

a) Each fraction in crude oil is mostly made of molecules containing only carbon and hydrogen. What name is given to these molecules?

(1 mark)

b) Copy and complete the following passage to explain how crude oil is separated into different fractions in the fractionating column. Use words from the box below. Each word can be used once, more than once or not at all.

gas	lower	down	higher	condense	up	boil	liquid

The crude oil is heated until most of it has turned into ....

The fractionating column has a temperature gradient and so when the substances

that make up crude oil reach a part of the column where the temperature is

.... than their boiling point, they ....

and drain off. Different fractions have different boiling points so they drain off

at different points as they move .... the column.

(4 marks)

c) Match the letters on the fractionating column below with the names of the different fractions shown in the box.

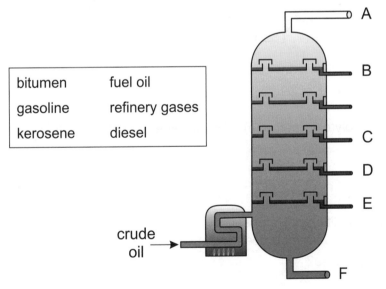

bitumen	fuel oil
gasoline	refinery gases
kerosene	diesel

(3 marks)

d) Name the fraction with the highest viscosity.

(1 mark)

e) Describe the link between the size of the molecules in crude oil fractions and their boiling points.

(1 mark)

f) State **one** use of fuel oil.

(1 mark)

SECTION 5 — CHEMISTRY IN INDUSTRY

Exam Questions

6   The equation below shows a polymerisation reaction to form poly(ethene).

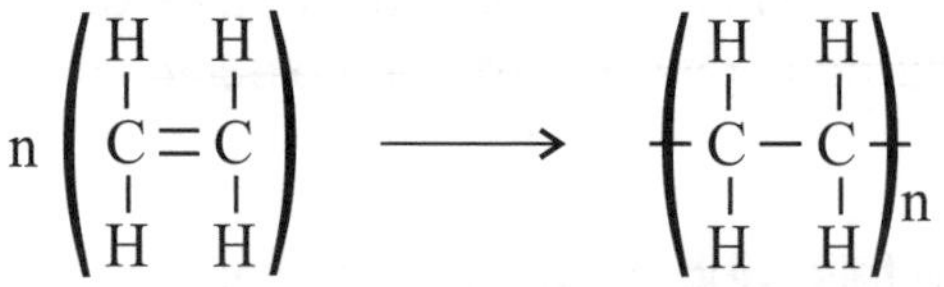

$$n \begin{pmatrix} \overset{\displaystyle H}{\underset{\displaystyle H}{\overset{|}{\underset{|}{C}}}} = \overset{\displaystyle H}{\underset{\displaystyle H}{\overset{|}{\underset{|}{C}}}} \end{pmatrix} \longrightarrow \begin{pmatrix} \overset{\displaystyle H}{\underset{\displaystyle H}{\overset{|}{\underset{|}{C}}}} - \overset{\displaystyle H}{\underset{\displaystyle H}{\overset{|}{\underset{|}{C}}}} \end{pmatrix}_n$$

a)   What is the name of the monomer used to form poly(ethene)?

(1 mark)

b)   The polymer poly(propene) can be made by addition polymerisation. The diagram below shows the displayed formula for part of a poly(propene) molecule.

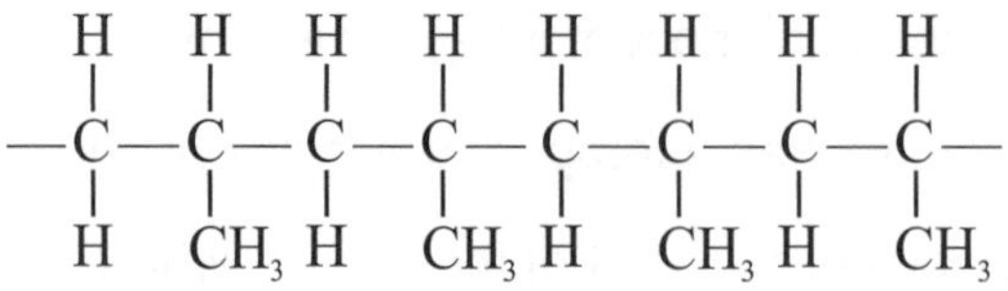

$$-\overset{\displaystyle H}{\underset{\displaystyle H}{\overset{|}{\underset{|}{C}}}} - \overset{\displaystyle H}{\underset{\displaystyle CH_3}{\overset{|}{\underset{|}{C}}}} - \overset{\displaystyle H}{\underset{\displaystyle H}{\overset{|}{\underset{|}{C}}}} - \overset{\displaystyle H}{\underset{\displaystyle CH_3}{\overset{|}{\underset{|}{C}}}} - \overset{\displaystyle H}{\underset{\displaystyle H}{\overset{|}{\underset{|}{C}}}} - \overset{\displaystyle H}{\underset{\displaystyle CH_3}{\overset{|}{\underset{|}{C}}}} - \overset{\displaystyle H}{\underset{\displaystyle H}{\overset{|}{\underset{|}{C}}}} - \overset{\displaystyle H}{\underset{\displaystyle CH_3}{\overset{|}{\underset{|}{C}}}} -$$

i)   Draw the structure of the monomer that is used to make poly(propene).

(1 mark)

ii)   Give the name of the monomer used to make poly(propene).

(1 mark)

PAPER 2

7   The diagram below shows the monomer that makes up poly(chloroethene) (PVC).

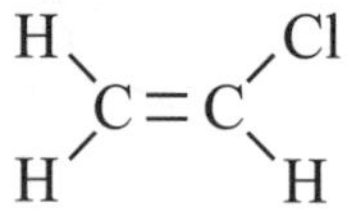

$$\overset{\displaystyle H}{\underset{\displaystyle H}{\diagdown}} C = C \overset{\diagup \displaystyle Cl}{\diagdown \displaystyle H}$$

a)   Draw the repeat unit for PVC.

(1 mark)

b)   Pipes can be made from poly(chloroethene). Give another use of this polymer.

(1 mark)

PAPER 2

8   Many polymers are formed by addition polymerisation.
    The polymer nylon is formed by a different process.
    a)   What is the name of this process?

(1 mark)

b)   The equation below shows two monomers joining together during the formation of nylon.

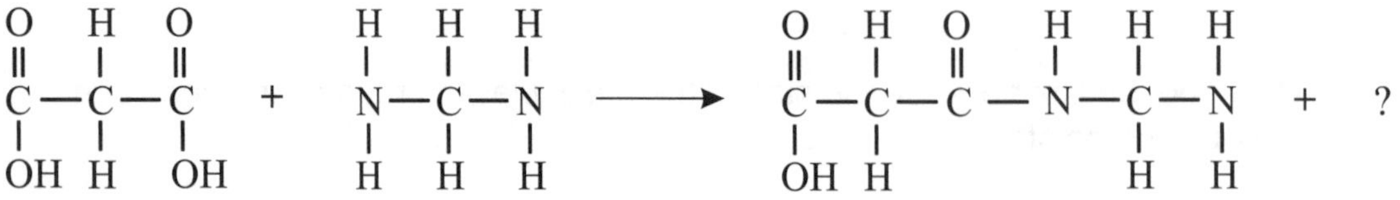

$$\overset{\displaystyle O}{\underset{\displaystyle OH}{\overset{\|}{\underset{|}{C}}}} - \overset{\displaystyle H}{\underset{\displaystyle H}{\overset{|}{\underset{|}{C}}}} - \overset{\displaystyle O}{\underset{\displaystyle OH}{\overset{\|}{\underset{|}{C}}}} \quad + \quad \overset{\displaystyle H}{\underset{\displaystyle H}{\overset{|}{\underset{|}{N}}}} - \overset{\displaystyle H}{\underset{\displaystyle H}{\overset{|}{\underset{|}{C}}}} - \overset{\displaystyle H}{\underset{\displaystyle H}{\overset{|}{\underset{|}{N}}}} \quad \longrightarrow \quad \overset{\displaystyle O}{\underset{\displaystyle OH}{\overset{\|}{\underset{|}{C}}}} - \overset{\displaystyle H}{\underset{\displaystyle H}{\overset{|}{\underset{|}{C}}}} - \overset{\displaystyle O}{\overset{\|}{C}} - \overset{\displaystyle H}{\underset{\displaystyle H}{\overset{|}{\underset{|}{N}}}} - \overset{\displaystyle H}{\underset{\displaystyle H}{\overset{|}{\underset{|}{C}}}} - \overset{\displaystyle H}{\underset{\displaystyle H}{\overset{|}{\underset{|}{N}}}} \quad + \quad ?$$

Name the second product of the reaction and give its chemical formula.

(2 marks)

The Haber Process

This is an important industrial process. It produces ammonia (NH_3), which is used to make fertilisers.

Nitrogen and Hydrogen are Needed to Make Ammonia

$$N_{2(g)} + 3H_{2(g)} \rightleftharpoons 2NH_{3(g)} \ (+ \text{ heat})$$

1) The nitrogen is obtained easily from the air, which is 78% nitrogen (and 21% oxygen).
2) The hydrogen comes from natural gas or from cracking hydrocarbons (see page 137).
3) Because the reaction is reversible (it occurs in both directions), not all of the nitrogen and hydrogen will convert to ammonia. The reaction reaches a dynamic equilibrium.

See page 123 for more on reversible reactions.

> **Industrial conditions**: pressure = 200 atmospheres; temperature = 450 °C; catalyst = iron.

The Reaction is Reversible, so a Compromise is needed:

1) Higher pressures favour the forward reaction (since there are four molecules of gas on the left-hand side for every two molecules on the right).

2) So the pressure is set as high as possible to give the best % yield, without making the plant too expensive to build. Hence the 200 atmospheres operating pressure.

3) The forward reaction is exothermic, which means that increasing the temperature will actually move the equilibrium the wrong way — away from ammonia and towards N_2 and H_2. So the yield of ammonia would be greater at lower temperatures.

4) The trouble is, lower temperatures mean a slower rate of reaction (and so equilibrium is reached more slowly). So they increase the temperature anyway, to get a much faster rate of reaction.

5) The 450 °C is a compromise between maximum yield and speed of reaction. It's better to wait just 20 seconds for a 10% yield than to have to wait 60 seconds for a 20% yield.

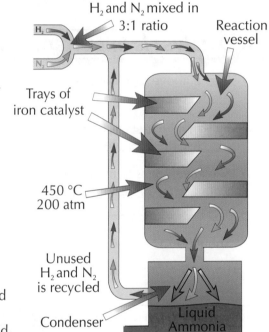

H₂ and N₂ mixed in 3:1 ratio

Reaction vessel

Trays of iron catalyst

450 °C 200 atm

Unused H₂ and N₂ is recycled

Condenser

Liquid Ammonia

6) The ammonia is formed as a gas, but as it cools in the condenser it liquefies and is removed. The unused hydrogen, H_2, and nitrogen, N_2, are recycled, so nothing is wasted.

7) The iron catalyst makes the reaction go faster, but doesn't affect the % yield.

Ammonia is Used to Make Nitric Acid and Ammonium Nitrate

1) Ammonia is used in the Ostwald process to make nitric acid (HNO_3).

2) You can also react ammonia with nitric acid, to get ammonium nitrate. Ammonium nitrate is an especially good fertiliser because it has nitrogen from two sources, the ammonia and the nitric acid. Kind of a double dose. Plants need nitrogen to make proteins.

3) Ammonium nitrate is a much more effective fertiliser than organic alternatives (e.g. pig poo), so it helps farmers produce crops from land that otherwise wouldn't have been fertile enough.

The Contact Process

The *Contact Process* is Used to Make *Sulfuric Acid*

1) The first stage of the contact process involves forming sulfur dioxide (SO_2) gas. This is usually done by burning sulfur in air or roasting sulfide ores.

$$S + O_2 \rightarrow SO_2$$

2) The sulfur dioxide is then oxidised (with the help of a catalyst) to form sulfur trioxide (SO_3) gas.

$$2SO_2 + O_2 \rightleftharpoons 2SO_3$$

3) Next, the sulfur trioxide is dissolved in concentrated sulfuric acid to form liquid oleum.

$$SO_3 + H_2SO_4 \rightarrow H_2S_2O_7$$

4) Finally, oleum is diluted with measured amounts of water to form concentrated sulfuric acid.

$$H_2S_2O_7 + H_2O \rightarrow 2H_2SO_4$$

A *Catalyst* is *Important* When Making SO_3

1) Step 2 above (oxidising SO_2 to SO_3) is exothermic (it gives out heat). Also, there are two moles of product compared to three moles of reactants (so the product has less volume than the reactants).

2) So to get the maximum yield, the obvious thing to do would be to reduce the temperature and increase the pressure. Unfortunately, reducing the temperature slows the reaction right down.

3) The key thing is to use a catalyst...
With a high temperature, a low-ish pressure and a vanadium(V) oxide catalyst, the reaction goes pretty quickly (and you get a good yield — about 99%). So this is what's done in practice.

> **Conditions for Contact Process**
> 1) Temperature: 450 °C.
> 2) Pressure: 2 atmospheres.
> 3) Catalyst: Vanadium(V) oxide, V_2O_5.

Modern Industry Uses Loads of *Sulfuric Acid*

Sulfuric acid is used in many manufacturing processes. For example, it's used to make:

- Fertilisers — sulfuric acid is mostly used to make phosphate fertilisers. Farmers use them to improve the amount of nutrients in the soil — this increases plant growth.

- Detergents — used for cleaning just about anything and everything.

- Paints — sulfuric acid is used to make titanium dioxide, which is a white pigment that's used in paints (and for drawing white lines on tennis courts).

---

450 °C, 2 atmospheres and V_2O_5 — perfect conditions...

...for the contact process, so make sure you know 'em. Making H_2SO_4 is the main aim of the contact process (but learn the other stages too). Then all that's left to learn are the various uses of sulfuric acid.

Electrolysis of Brine

Electrolysis of brine (sodium chloride solution) was covered briefly in Section 1 on page 51.
This page goes into a bit more detail, and yes, you do need to know the details. Sorry 'bout that.

Electrolysis of Salt gives Hydrogen, Chlorine and NaOH

Concentrated brine (sodium chloride solution) is electrolysed
industrially using a diaphragm cell a bit like this one:

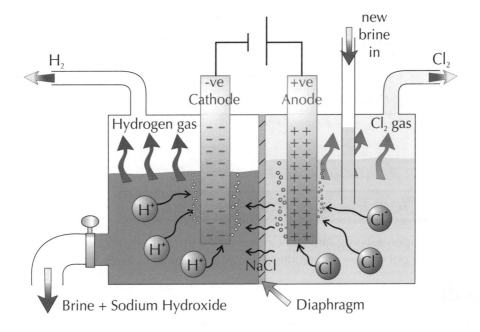

It produces three useful products:

1. Hydrogen gas

Hydrogen gas is given off at the cathode — two hydrogen
ions accept two electrons to become one hydrogen molecule.

2. Chlorine gas

Chlorine gas is given off at the anode — two chloride ions
(Cl^-) lose their electrons and become one chlorine molecule.

3. Sodium ions

The sodium ions (Na^+) stay in solution and the hydroxide ions (OH^-) from the water
are also left behind. This means that sodium hydroxide is left in the solution.

I reckon it'd be pretty useful to remember that picture...

...so cover the page and practise drawing it out till you get it spot on. The industrial electrolysis of
brine started as a way to make sodium hydroxide and used mercury as one of the electrodes. But this
caused big environmental problems, so cells like the diaphragm cell above are used today.

Electrolysis of Brine

You need to know the reactions that go on at the <u>anode</u> and the <u>cathode</u> during the electrolysis of brine.

The **Half-Equations** — *Make Sure the* **Electrons Balance**

You can write out <u>half-equations</u> for the reactions that take place at the <u>anode</u> and the <u>cathode</u>. The main thing is to make sure the <u>number of electrons</u> is the <u>same</u> for <u>both half-equations</u>. For the electrolysis of sodium chloride the half-equations are:

$$\underline{\text{Cathode:}} \quad 2H^+ \ + \ 2e^- \ \rightarrow \ H_2$$

$$\underline{\text{Anode:}} \quad 2Cl^- \ \rightarrow \ Cl_2 \ + \ 2e^-$$

There's more about half-equations on page 49.

Useful Products from the **Electrolysis of Brine**

With all that effort and expense going into the electrolysis of brine, there'd better be some pretty useful stuff coming out of it — and so there is... and you have to learn it all too. Ace.

1. **Chlorine**

Chlorine is used to <u>sterilise water supplies</u> (chlorination). It's also used to make <u>bleach</u> and <u>HCl</u>.

2. **Hydrogen**

Hydrogen is used in the <u>Haber process</u> and to change <u>oils</u> into <u>fats</u> for making <u>margarine</u>.

3. **Sodium Hydroxide**

Sodium hydroxide is a very strong <u>base</u> and is used <u>widely</u> in the <u>chemical industry</u>. For example, it's used to make <u>soap</u>, <u>bleach</u> and <u>paper pulp</u>.

Brine — it's not just for keeping tuna in...

Wowie. Who knew salty water could be so useful... The products of brine electrolysis are just the sort of thing that examiners like to test on, so make sure you know exactly what each product is used for. Learning the half-equations is a good idea too — and make sure you remember to balance them.

Warm-Up and Exam Questions

That's it then, Chemistry in Industry all done and dusted... Almost, but first you need to check that you know it all. Give these last few pages of questions a go and see how you get on...

Warm-Up Questions

1) What two things are needed to manufacture ammonia?
2) True or false? The forward reaction in the Haber process is exothermic.
3) True or false? The Haber process is used to make soap.

Exam Questions

PAPER 2

1   The contact process is used to manufacture sulfuric acid.
    Copy and complete the table below with the conditions used in the contact process.

Temperature	
Pressure	
Catalyst	

(3 marks)

PAPER 2

2   The contact process involves several different reactions.
    Copy, complete and balance the following equations involved in the contact process,
    and briefly describe each step of the process.

a) Step 1
    Equation: .... + ... $\longrightarrow$ SO_2

(2 marks)

b) Step 2
    Equation: .... + ... $\rightleftharpoons$ SO_3

(3 marks)

c) Step 3
    Equation: SO_3 + ... $\longrightarrow$ ....

(2 marks)

d) Step 4
    Equation: .... + ... $\longrightarrow$ H_2SO_4

(3 marks)

PAPER 2

3   Sulfuric acid has lots of different uses in industry.
    Give **three** uses of sulfuric acid made in the contact process.

(3 marks)

Exam Questions

4   The Haber process is carried out under a specific set of conditions.

   a) Identify the industrial conditions used in the production of ammonia from the
       boxes below.

Temperature (°C)	200	350	450	800	1000
Pressure (atmospheres)	200	300	450	700	1000

   (2 marks)

   b) Name the catalyst used in the Haber process.

   (1 mark)

   c) In the Haber process, gases pass through a reaction chamber before entering
       a cooling chamber.

       Explain how cooling the gases allows ammonia to be separated from unused
       hydrogen and nitrogen, and state what happens to these unused gases.

   (3 marks)

PAPER 2

5   The electrolysis of brine generates products that can be used in industry for the manufacture
     of a variety of different chemicals and household goods.
     A company carries out large-scale electrolysis of brine.
     The table below shows the final uses of the electrolysis products the company sells.

Final use	Percentage of company's electrolysis output used for this purpose
hydrochloric acid	29%
margarine	19%
soap	?
other	35%

   a) What percentage of the company's output is used for the manufacture of soap?

   (1 mark)

   b) State the product of brine electrolysis that is used in the manufacture of
       the following products.

       i)   hydrochloric acid

   (1 mark)

       ii)   paper pulp

   (1 mark)

       iii) soap

   (1 mark)

   c) Which **two** products of brine electrolysis can be used in the manufacture
       of bleach?

   (2 marks)

   d) Name the product of brine electrolysis that can be used in the sterilisation
       of water supplies.

   (1 mark)

Exam Questions

6   The Haber process is used to make ammonia, which is widely used in industry.

   a)   Complete the chemical equation for the reaction.

$$\ldots\ldots\ldots + \ldots\ldots\ldots \rightleftharpoons 2NH_3$$

(2 marks)

   b)   State the name of the two reactants in the forward reaction and a source of each one.

(4 marks)

   c)   Name **two** things that are manufactured using ammonia.

(2 marks)

PAPER 2

7   The electrolysis of brine is carried out on a large scale industrially.

   a)   The process uses concentrated brine. What is brine a solution of?

(1 mark)

   b)   The diagram below shows a diaphragm cell used for the electrolysis of brine.

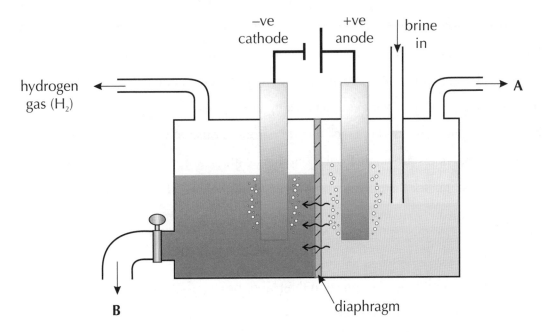

Name the products of this reaction and identify which location on the diagram, **A** or **B**, they are collected from.

(4 marks)

   c)   Different reactions take place at each of the electrodes in the diaphragm cell.

      i)   Write a half-equation for the reaction at the negative electrode, and describe what happens during the reaction.

(3 marks)

      ii)   Write a half-equation for the reaction at the positive electrode, and describe what happens during the reaction.

(3 marks)

Revision Summary for Section 5

It's the end of the last section, woooo. And what a section — full of industrial-sized processes and reactions that are going to take an industrial amount of learning to remember. But don't panic, because I have just the thing to help you on your way — it's the revision summary. Keep going through the questions until you can get all the answers without having to look back at the section.

1) Are metal oxides reduced or oxidised to obtain the metal from them?
   What role does carbon play in this reaction?

2) What method of extraction would you use for a) magnesium, b) iron?

3) Why is cryolite used in the electrolysis of aluminium?

4) Why does molten aluminium oxide conduct electricity?

5) What are the three raw materials used to extract iron from its ore?

6) Write out word equations for the three reactions that are used to extract iron.

7) Suggest one use for iron and state the property of iron that makes it suitable for that use.

8) Suggest one use for aluminium and state the property that makes it suitable for that use.

9) What is crude oil a mixture of?

10) Describe how fractional distillation is used to separate crude oil into fractions.

11) Name five fractions of crude oil and what they're used for.

12) Explain how nitrogen oxides are formed from burning fuels. Where is this likely to happen?

13) What conditions are needed for the production of carbon monoxide when a fuel is burnt?

14) How do the boiling points of hydrocarbons change as the chain length gets longer?

15) What is cracking? Why do we need to crack hydrocarbons?

16) What are the conditions used to crack a hydrocarbon industrially?

17) What kind of polymers are made from monomers with a carbon-carbon double bond?

18) Draw the repeat unit for the polymer on the right.

19) What kind of polymers are made when a small
    molecule is released during the reaction?

$$\begin{array}{ccccccc} H & H & H & H & H & H \\ | & | & | & | & | & | \\ -C & -C & -C & -C & -C & -C- \\ | & | & | & | & | & | \\ H & Cl & H & Cl & H & Cl \end{array}$$

20) Give one use for poly(ethene).

21) Write out the reaction that takes place in the Haber process.

22) What are the industrial conditions used in the Haber process?

23) What does the contact process produce?

24) What are the industrial conditions used for the contact process?

25) Sketch a picture of a diaphragm cell that is used to electrolyse brine. Label the anode, cathode, diaphragm, where the brine enters the cell and where the products leave the cell.

26) Write out the half-equations that take place at the anode and the cathode when brine is electrolysed.

27) Give two uses of chlorine and two uses of sodium hydroxide.

Experimental Know-How

<u>Scientists</u> need to know how to <u>plan</u> and <u>carry out scientific experiments</u>. Unfortunately, the examiners think <u>you</u> should be able to do the same. But don't worry — that's what this section's all about.

You Might Get Asked Questions on **Reliability** and **Validity**

1) <u>RELIABLE</u> results come from <u>experiments</u> that give the <u>same data</u>:

> - each time the experiment is <u>repeated</u> (by you),
> - each time the experiment is <u>reproduced</u> by <u>other scientists</u>.

2) <u>VALID</u> results are both <u>reliable</u> AND come from <u>experiments</u> that were designed to be a <u>fair test</u>.

In the exam, you could be asked to suggest ways to <u>improve</u> the <u>reliability</u> or <u>validity</u> of some <u>experimental results</u>. If so, there are a couple of things to think about:

1) *Controlling Variables* Improves *Validity*

1) A variable is something that has the potential to <u>change</u>, e.g. temperature.
    In a lab experiment you usually <u>change one variable</u> and <u>measure</u> how it affects <u>another variable</u>.

> EXAMPLE: you might change <u>only</u> the temperature of a chemical reaction and measure how this affects the rate of reaction.

2) To make it a <u>fair test</u>, <u>everything else</u> that could affect the results should <u>stay the same</u> — otherwise you can't tell if the thing you're changing is causing the results or not.

> EXAMPLE continued: you need to keep the concentration of the reactants the same, otherwise you won't know if any change in the rate of reaction is caused by the change in temperature, or a difference in reactant concentration.

3) The variable you CHANGE is called the INDEPENDENT variable.

4) The variable you MEASURE is called the DEPENDENT variable.

5) The variables that you KEEP THE SAME are called CONTROL variables.

> EXAMPLE continued:
> Independent variable = temperature   Dependent variable = rate of reaction
> Control variables = concentration of reactants, volume/mass of reactants, etc.

6) Because you can't always control all the variables, you often need to use a CONTROL EXPERIMENT — an experiment that's kept under the <u>same conditions</u> as the rest of the investigation, but doesn't have anything done to it. This is so that you can see what happens when you don't change anything at all.

2) *Carrying Out Repeats* Improves *Reliability*

To improve reliability you need to <u>repeat</u> any measurements you make and calculate the <u>mean</u> (average). You need to repeat each measurement at least <u>three times</u>.

Getting reliable and valid results is very important

You might be asked to <u>suggest</u> what variables need to be controlled in an experiment. For example, you know that <u>paper chromatography</u> is affected by the <u>solvent</u> and the <u>paper</u> you use, so these variables need to be kept constant (providing you're not investigating one of them). You might also need to say <u>how</u> you'd control the variables, e.g. the temperature could be controlled using a <u>water bath</u>.

Experimental Know-How

You Might Have to Suggest Ways to Make an Experiment Safer

1) It's important that experiments are safe. If you're asked to suggest ways to make an experiment safer, you'll first need to identify what the <u>potential hazards</u> might be. Hazards include things like:

- <u>Chemicals</u>, e.g. sulfuric acid can burn your skin and alcohols catch fire easily.
- <u>Fire</u>, e.g. an unattended Bunsen burner is a fire hazard.
- <u>Electricity</u>, e.g. faulty electrical equipment could give you a shock.

2) Then you'll need to suggest ways of <u>reducing</u> the <u>risks</u> involved with the hazard, e.g.

- If you're working with <u>sulfuric acid</u>, always wear gloves and safety goggles. This will reduce the risk of the acid coming into contact with your skin and eyes.
- If you're using a <u>Bunsen burner</u>, stand it on a heat proof mat. This will reduce the risk of starting a fire.
- If you're working with <u>chemicals</u> that give off <u>harmful gases</u>, you need to use a fume cupboard. This will reduce the risk of you breathing in the gases.

You Could be Asked About Accuracy...

1) It's important that results are <u>ACCURATE</u>. Really accurate results are those that are <u>really close</u> to the <u>true answer</u>.

2) The accuracy of your results usually depends on your <u>method</u>.

E.g. say you wanted to measure the <u>rate</u> of a <u>chemical reaction</u> that releases a <u>gas</u> as a product. The rate of the reaction would be the <u>amount of gas produced per unit time</u>. You could <u>estimate</u> how much gas is produced by <u>counting</u> the number of <u>bubbles</u> that are released. But the bubbles could be <u>different sizes</u>, and if they're produced really quickly you might <u>miss some</u> when counting. It would be more accurate to <u>collect the gas</u> (e.g. using a gas syringe) and <u>measure</u> its <u>volume</u>.

3) To make your results as <u>accurate</u> as possible, you need to make sure you're measuring the <u>right thing</u> and that you <u>don't miss</u> anything or <u>include</u> anything that shouldn't be included in the measurements.

E.g. if you're measuring the volume of gas produced using a gas syringe, you need to make sure the syringe is <u>empty</u> at the start of the experiment. If there's any air in it the reading will be <u>wrong</u>.

...And Precision

1) Results also need to be <u>PRECISE</u>. Precise results are those taken using <u>sensitive instruments</u> that measure in <u>small increments</u>, e.g. using a ruler with a millimetre scale gives more precise data than using a ruler with a scale in centimetres.

2) By recording your results to a <u>greater number</u> of <u>decimal places</u>, you'll increase their precision, e.g.

In some exam questions, you'll be told how precise to be in your answer. So if you're told to give an answer to 2 decimal places, make sure you do or you could lose marks.

Repeat	Data set 1	Data set 2
1	12	11.98
2	14	14.00
3	13	13.01

The results in data set 2 are more precise than those in data set 1.

Safety first — goggles on before you read this book...

Sometimes you'll be asked to <u>describe</u> how you'd carry out your <u>own experiment</u> in the exam. All this stuff about reliability and what not will apply then too. So make sure you learn it and write it down.

Drawing Graphs and Interpreting Results

If you're presented with some results from an experiment you've got to know <u>what to do with them</u>.

You Should Be Able to Identify *Anomalous Results*

1) Most results vary a bit, but any that are <u>totally different</u> are called <u>anomalous results</u>.

2) They're <u>caused</u> by <u>human errors</u>, e.g. by a mistake made when measuring or by not setting up a piece of equipment properly.

3) You could be asked to <u>identify</u> an anomalous result in the exam and suggest what <u>caused</u> it — just look for a result that <u>doesn't fit in</u> with the rest (e.g. it's <u>too high</u> or <u>too low</u>) then try to figure out what could have <u>gone wrong</u> with the experiment to have caused it.

4) If you're calculating an <u>average</u>, you can <u>ignore</u> any anomalous results.

You Need to Be Able to *Draw Graphs...*

In the exam, you might be asked to draw a <u>graph</u> or <u>bar chart</u> from a set of results. If you're not told which one to go for, here's how you decide:

1) If the independent variable is <u>categoric</u> (comes in distinct categories, e.g. ion charge, metals) you should use a <u>bar chart</u> to display the data.

2) If the independent variable is <u>continuous</u> (can take any value within a range, e.g. length, volume, time) you should use a <u>line graph</u> to display the data.

Here are a few useful tips for <u>drawing line graphs</u>:

Remember to <u>label</u> the axes and include the <u>units</u>.

The <u>dependent</u> variable (the thing you measure) goes on the <u>y-axis</u> (the <u>vertical</u> one).

The <u>independent</u> variable (the thing you change) goes on the <u>x-axis</u> (the <u>horizontal</u> one).

When plotting points, use a <u>sharp pencil</u> and make a <u>neat little cross</u> (don't do blobs).

nice clear mark / smudged unclear marks

If you're told to <u>join up the points</u> using a <u>straight line</u>, use a <u>ruler</u> to draw a neat line between each point.

If you're told to draw a <u>line of best fit</u>, try to draw the line <u>through</u> or as <u>near</u> to <u>as many points as possible</u>, ignoring anomalous results. This graph shows a line of best fit.

Graph to Show Product Formed Against Time — Product formed (cm^3) vs Time (s) — anomalous result

Make sure you fill <u>at least half</u> of the space you're given to draw a graph.

...And *Interpret* Them

1) A graph is used to show the <u>relationship</u> between two variables — you need to be able to look at a graph and <u>describe</u> this relationship. For example, the graph above shows that as <u>time goes on</u>, <u>more product is formed</u>.

2) You also need to be able to <u>read information</u> off a graph. In this example, if you wanted to know how much product had been formed by <u>11 s</u>, you'd draw a <u>vertical line up</u> from the x-axis at 11 s and a <u>horizontal line across</u> to the y-axis. This would tell you that the amount of product formed by 11 s was around <u>9.7 cm^3</u>.

You might have to describe the results in a table...

...or pick out an anomalous result from one. You'll also be expected to do <u>basic maths</u>, like <u>calculating</u> a <u>mean</u> (add everything together and divide by the total number of values) or a <u>percentage</u>.

Planning Experiments and Evaluating Conclusions

In the exam, you could be asked to <u>plan</u> or <u>describe</u> how you'd <u>carry out</u> an experiment. The experiment might be one you've already come across or you might be asked to come up with an <u>experiment of your own</u> to test something. You might also be asked to say what you think of someone else's <u>conclusion</u>.

You Need to Be Able to Plan a **Good Experiment**

Here are some <u>general tips</u> on what to include when planning an experiment:

1) Say <u>what</u> you're <u>measuring</u> (i.e. what the <u>dependent variable</u> is going to be).

2) Say <u>what</u> you're <u>changing</u> (i.e. what the <u>independent variable</u> is going to be) and describe <u>how</u> you're going to change it.

3) Describe the <u>method</u> and the <u>apparatus</u> you'd use.

4) Describe what <u>variables</u> you're keeping <u>constant</u> — and <u>how</u> you're going to do it.

5) Say that you need to <u>repeat</u> the experiment at least three times, to make the results <u>more reliable</u>.

6) Say whether you're using a <u>control</u> or not.

Here's an <u>idea</u> of the sort of thing you might be asked in the exam and what you might write as an answer.

Exam-style Question:

1 Describe an experiment to investigate the effect of concentration on the reaction of dilute hydrochloric acid and magnesium metal. (6)

Example Answer:

In this experiment you should change the concentration of the dilute hydrochloric acid. You can see what effect this has by measuring the mass of the reaction mixture.

Set up a flask containing a measured mass of magnesium metal. Place the flask on a mass balance.

Pour a measured volume of dilute hydrochloric acid into the flask and start the timer. Take readings of the mass at regular time intervals until the mass doesn't change anymore. The mass of gas lost from the reaction mixture can be calculated using this data.

Carry out the experiment again with different concentrations of dilute hydrochloric acid (e.g. 0.1 mol/dm³, 0.2 mol/dm³, 0.3 mol/dm³ and 0.4 mol/dm³).

The mass should be measured at the same time intervals for each acid concentration. The volume of acid should always be the same and the same mass of magnesium metal should be used each time. The temperature must also remain constant.

Repeat the experiment three times at each acid concentration and use the results to find the average mass of gas lost at each time interval for each concentration.

You could also collect the hydrogen in a gas syringe and measure its volume.

You Could Be Asked to **Evaluate** a **Conclusion**

1) In the exam, you could be given an experimental <u>conclusion</u> and asked to <u>evaluate</u> it.

2) This just means saying whether or not you think <u>evidence</u> from the experiment <u>supports</u> the conclusion — and <u>why</u>.

Plan your way to exam success...

The number of marks available for a question like this will vary, but it'll usually be around five or six. <u>Think</u> about what you're going to say <u>beforehand</u>. You don't want to <u>forget</u> something <u>important</u>.

Practice Papers

Once you've been through all the questions in this book, you should feel pretty confident about the exams. As final preparation, here is a set of **practice papers** to really get you set for the real thing. These papers are designed to give you the best possible preparation for your exams.

Candidate Surname	Candidate Forename(s)

Centre Number	Candidate Number

Certificate
International GCSE

Chemistry
Paper 1C

Practice Paper
Time allowed: 2 hours

You must have:
- A ruler.
- A calculator.

Total marks:

Instructions to candidates
- Use **black** ink to write your answers.
- Write your name and other details in the spaces provided above.
- Answer **all** questions in the spaces provided.
- In calculations, show clearly how you worked out your answers.
- You will need to answer some questions by placing a cross in a box, like this: ☒
  To change your answer, draw a line through the box like this: ☒
  Then mark your new answer as normal.

Information for candidates
- The marks available are given in brackets at the end of each question.
- There are 120 marks available for this paper.
- You might find the periodic table on the inside of the front cover useful.

Advice for candidates
- Read all the questions carefully.
- Write your answers as clearly and neatly as possible.
- Keep in mind how much time you have left.

Answer **all** questions

1   Atoms contain protons, neutrons and electrons.

(a)   Complete the table to show the relative charges and relative masses of protons, neutrons and electrons.

[2]

Particle	Mass	Charge
Proton	1	+1
Neutron	*1*	*0*
Electron	*1/2000*	*−1*

(b)   The table below shows the numbers of protons, neutrons and electrons in six different atoms.

Atom	Number of protons	Number of neutrons	Number of electrons
A	5	6	5
B	7	7	7
C	6	8	6
D	6	6	6
E	10	10	10
F	4	5	4

Which **two** atoms are isotopes of the same element? Explain your answer.

Atoms .... and ....

Explanation ....

....

[2]

Zinc appears in the periodic table as shown below.

65

Zn

Zinc

30

(c) How many protons, neutrons and electrons are there in an atom of zinc?

Protons .... Neutrons .... Electrons ....

[3]

(d) Zinc sulfate is a compound with the formula $ZnSO_4$.

(i) What is a compound?

....

....

[2]

(ii) Calculate the relative formula mass of zinc sulfate.

....

[2]

[Total 11 marks]

Turn over ▶

158

2 Nitrogen dioxide is an atmospheric pollutant.

(a) Suggest why nitrogen dioxide levels can be particularly high in cities.

....

....

....

....

[2]

(b) Nitrogen dioxide can react with water in the atmosphere to form nitric acid, which falls as acid rain. Acid rain can damage buildings made from limestone, which is mainly calcium carbonate.

(i) Complete the word equation for the reaction between nitric acid and calcium carbonate.

nitric acid + calcium carbonate →

.... + ... + ...

[2]

(ii) Name **one** other gas that can cause acid rain.

....

[1]

(iii) Give **one** problem, other than damage to buildings, caused by acid rain.

....

[1]

[Total 6 marks]

3   The halogens make up Group 7 of the periodic table.
     The table below shows some of the physical properties of the first four halogens.

Halogen	Atomic number	Melting Point (°C)	Boiling Point (°C)	Colour at room temperature
Fluorine	9	−220	−188	very pale yellow
Chlorine	17		−34	green
Bromine	35	−7	59	
Iodine	53	114	185	dark grey

(a) (i) Predict the melting point of chlorine, using the data in the table.
         Place a cross (x) in the appropriate box to indicate your answer.

         ☐ −231 °C

         ☐ −216 °C

         ☐ −101 °C

         ☐ 107 °C

                                                                                    [1]

    (ii) Explain your answer to part i).

         ....

         ....
                                                                                    [1]

(b)   Describe the appearance of bromine at room temperature.

       ....
                                                                                    [2]

(c)   Write down the balanced symbol equation for the reaction between bromine and
       potassium iodide.

       ....Br⁻...+...K⁺ I⁻...
                                                                                    [2]

Turn over ▶

(d) (i) Complete the diagram below to show the electronic structure of a chlorine atom. Mark each electron using an 'X'.

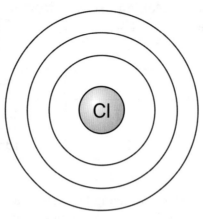

[1]

(ii) Explain how the group number of chlorine in the periodic table is related to its electronic structure.

....

....

....

[2]

(e) Chlorine is bubbled through sodium iodide solution. What will happen? Explain your answer in terms of the relative positions of chlorine and iodine in the periodic table.

................$Cl_2 +$ $Na I$ $\rightarrow$ ....

....

....

....

....

[3]

(f) Chlorine can combine with hydrogen to form hydrogen chloride. Explain why hydrogen chloride forms an acidic solution in water.

....

....

....

[2]

[Total 14 marks]

4　A student wanted to find out which of five dyes could be present in a particular black ink.

(a)　The student was asked to suggest a method. This is the method the student suggested:

- Take a piece of filter paper. Draw a pencil line near the bottom.

- Add spots of the dyes to the line at regular intervals.

- Put the paper into a beaker of water with the line just touching the water.

- Repeat these steps with a spot of the black ink on a second piece of filter paper, and put this paper into a beaker of ethanol.

- Place a lid on each beaker, and wait for the solvents to travel to the top of the paper.

- Compare the positions of the spots created by the black ink with those created by the dyes.

Identify **two** problems with this method. For each problem, suggest how you would alter the method to carry out the experiment correctly.

You can assume the student takes sensible safety precautions.

Problem 1 ....

....

....

Correction ....

....

....

....

Problem 2 ....

....

Correction ....

....

....

....

[4]

Turn over ▶

(b)   The student repeated the experiment using the correct method.
The results are shown below.

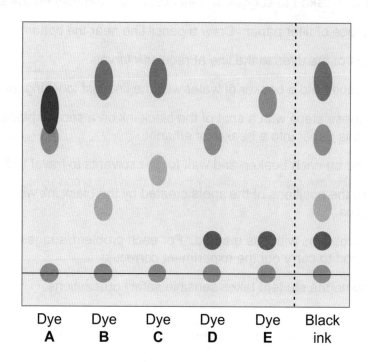

Dye   Dye   Dye   Dye   Dye   Black
A   **B**   **C**   **D**   **E**   ink

Which dyes (**A-E**) could have been present in the black ink? Explain your answer.

Dyes ....

Explanation ....

....

....

....

[2]

[Total 6 marks]

5 Carbon dioxide is a simple molecule whose displayed formula is shown below.

$$O=C=O$$

(a) Why does carbon dioxide have a low melting point?

....

....

[1]

(b) Draw a dot and cross diagram to show the bonding in carbon dioxide.
Only show the outer electrons.

[2]

(c) Explain how the properties of carbon dioxide make it useful for extinguishing fires.

....

....

....

[2]

(d) Another compound containing carbon is made up of 96.0 g of calcium, 28.8 g of carbon and 115.2 g of oxygen.
Calculate the empirical formula of the compound.

Empirical formula = ...

[3]

Turn over ▶

164

(e) Carbon dioxide can be produced by heating zinc carbonate ($ZnCO_3$).
Zinc oxide (ZnO) is left behind.

(i) State the name for this type of reaction.

....
[1]

(ii) Suggest how you could collect the carbon dioxide produced in this experiment.

....

....
[1]

(f) Which of the following sentences correctly describes the solubility of carbon dioxide in water? Place a cross (x) in the appropriate box to indicate your answer.

☐ Carbon dioxide is insoluble in water, but becomes soluble under pressure.

☐ Carbon dioxide is slightly soluble in water, but becomes less soluble under pressure.

☐ Carbon dioxide is slightly soluble in water, but becomes more soluble under pressure.

☐ Carbon dioxide is very soluble in water, but becomes less soluble under pressure.
[1]

(g) Carbon dioxide is a greenhouse gas.

(i) What is meant by the term **greenhouse gas**?

....

....

....
[2]

(ii) What percentage of the air is made up of carbon dioxide?

....
[1]

(iii) Give **one** possible effect of increasing the amount of carbon dioxide in the atmosphere.

....

....
[1]
[Total 15 marks]

6 Analytical tests can be used to identify different substances.

(a) Suggest tests that could be used to distinguish between the following pairs of compounds in solution. You should describe the tests and the results expected for each solution.

[4]

Solution A	Solution B	Description of test	Observations	
			Solution A	Solution B
iron(II) chloride	iron(III) chloride	....	....	....
sodium chloride	sodium iodide	....	....	....

(b) When an unknown compound is placed in a blue Bunsen flame, it gives a yellow-orange colour. If dilute acid is added to the compound, a gas is produced. When this gas is bubbled through limewater, the limewater goes cloudy.

Identify the compound by its chemical name.

....

[2]

[Total 6 marks]

Turn over ▶

7   The displayed formulae of two gases are shown below.

Gas **A**   H—C—C—C—H   Gas **B**   H—C—C=C

(a)   Name gas **B**.

....

[1]

(b)   Pentane is a saturated compound. Draw the displayed formula of pentane.

[1]

(c)   What name is given to unsaturated hydrocarbons like gas **B**?

....

[1]

(d)   Describe a test that you could use to distinguish between gas **A** and gas **B**.
        State what you would observe in each case.

Test: ....

Observations:

Gas **A**: ....

Gas **B**: ....

[2]

(e)   In terms of bond breaking and bond formation, explain the observation for gas **B**.

....

....

....

[2]

(f)   Gas **A** is burnt in a plentiful supply of oxygen.
        Write a balanced chemical equation for this reaction.

....

[2]

[Total 9 marks]

8   Metals can be extracted from their oxides using several different methods.

(a)   Copper can be extracted from its oxide in a reduction reaction using carbon.
State what is meant by a **reduction reaction**.

....

....
[1]

(b)   Aluminium is extracted from aluminium oxide by electrolysis.

(i)   Explain why aluminium cannot be extracted by reduction with carbon.

....

....
[1]

(ii)   The aluminium oxide is dissolved in molten cryolite for the electrolysis reaction.
Explain why.

....

....
[2]

(iii)   Write the half-equations for the reactions that occur at each electrode.

Negative electrode ....

Positive electrode ....
[4]

(iv)   The positive electrode is made from carbon. Explain why it has to be regularly replaced.

....

....
[1]

[Total 9 marks]

168

9   Self-heating cans use exothermic chemical reactions to heat up their contents.
     When a seal is broken two chemicals mix and react, heating up the can.
     Calcium oxide and water can be used to heat up drinks in this way.

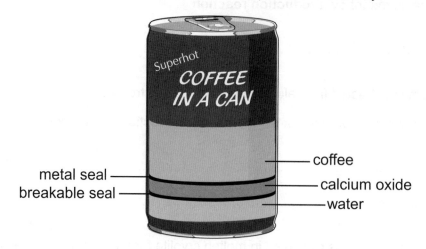

(a)   What is an exothermic reaction?

       ....

       ....

                                                                                                                            [1]

(b)   A student wanted to test the reaction of different substances with water
       to see if they could be used to cool drinks down.

       Outline an experiment the student could carry out to test different substances.

       ....

       ....

       ....

       ....

       ....

                                                                                                                            [3]

(c)   Calcium oxide (CaO) is produced when iron(III) oxide (Fe_2O_3) reacts with calcium.
       Iron is also produced. Write a balanced chemical equation for this reaction.

       ....

                                                                                                                            [2]
                                                                                                            [Total 6 marks]

10 The graph shows the volume of gas produced over time when lumps of zinc are reacted with dilute sulfuric acid.

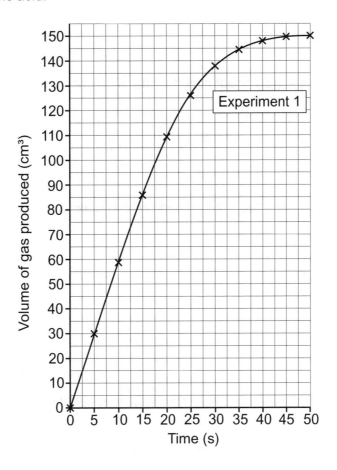

In a second experiment, some copper sulfate catalyst was added to the acid.
The same amount of zinc was used as before, and the lumps were of a similar size.
The same volume of dilute sulfuric acid was also used.
The results are shown in the table.

| Time | Volume of gas formed (cm³) |
(secs)	Experiment 2
0	0
5	50
10	100
15	130
20	143
25	148
30	150
35	150
40	150
45	150
50	150

(a) Plot the results of the second experiment on the graph above.

Draw a curve of best fit through the points. Label the line 'Experiment 2'.

[2]

Turn over ▶

(b)   How long does it take to form half of the total amount of gas collected
       in the second experiment?

       ....

                                                                                        [1]

(c)   What do the curves show about how the rate of reaction changes as
       the reaction proceeds?

       ....

                                                                                        [1]

(d)   State how the catalyst affects the reaction rate and explain how you can tell this from
       the graph.

       ....

       ....

       ....

                                                                                        [1]

(e)   Explain, in terms of activation energy, how catalysts affect reaction rates.

       ....

       ....

       ....

                                                                                        [1]
                                                                                [Total 6 marks]

11   Titration with 0.050 mol/dm³ sulfuric acid was used to determine the concentration of calcium hydroxide solution. In the titration, 8.80 cm³ of sulfuric acid were needed to neutralise 10.0 cm³ of the calcium hydroxide solution.

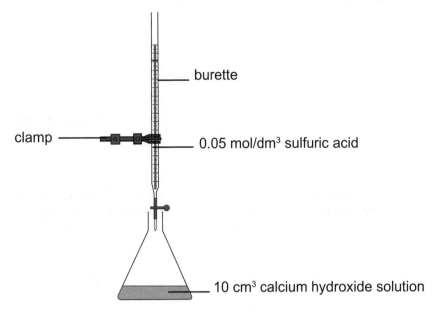

burette

clamp — 0.05 mol/dm³ sulfuric acid

10 cm³ calcium hydroxide solution

(a)   Name a suitable indicator for the titration.

....

[1]

(b)   Complete and balance the equation for this reaction below.

$H_2SO_{4(aq)}$ + $Ca(OH)_{2(aq)}$ → ....$_{(aq)}$ + ...$H_2O_{(l)}$

[2]

(c) (i)   How many moles of sulfuric acid reacted with the calcium hydroxide in the titration?

Number of moles = ...

[1]

    (ii)   How many moles of calcium hydroxide reacted with the acid?

....

[1]

    (iii) Calculate the concentration of the calcium hydroxide solution in mol/dm³.
        Show clearly how you work out your answer.

Concentration = ... mol/dm³

[1]

Turn over ▶

(iv) Calculate the concentration of the calcium hydroxide solution in g/dm^3.
The M_r for calcium hydroxide is 74.

Show clearly how you work out your answer.

Concentration = ... g/dm^3
[1]

(d) The pH curve below shows the change in pH that occurred during a second titration where sodium hydroxide was being added to a weak acid.

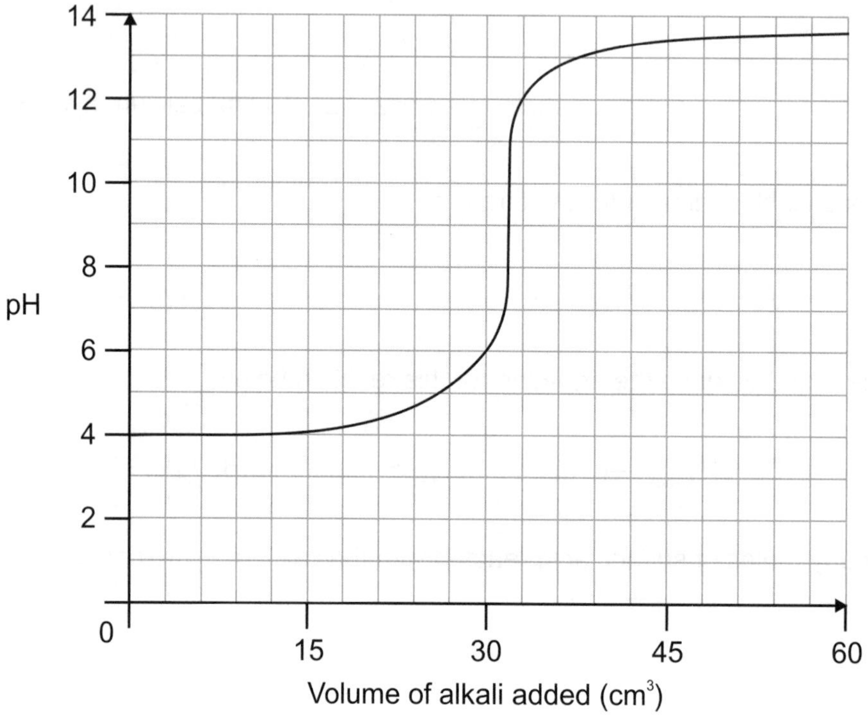

(i) What was the volume of sodium hydroxide solution at neutralisation?

....
[1]

(ii) What was the pH of the solution when 46.0 cm^3 of sodium hydroxide was added?

....
[1]

[Total 9 marks]

12   Iron pipes need protection from rusting.

(a)   What conditions cause iron to rust?

....

....

[2]

(b)   Rusting is a type of corrosion. What causes corrosion?
Place a cross (x) in the appropriate box to indicate your answer.

☐   distillation

☐   electrolysis

☐   oxidation

☐   reduction

[1]

(c)   Paint can be used to stop underground iron pipes rusting, but they will eventually need repainting or replacing. An alternative to this is to connect a large piece of magnesium to the pipe, as shown in the diagram below.

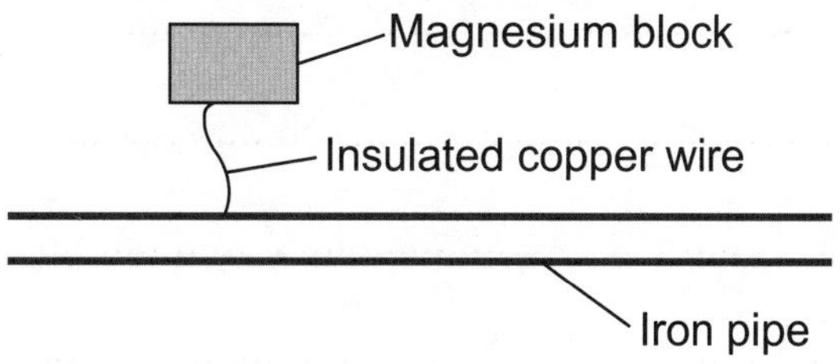

(i)   What name is given to this kind of corrosion protection?

....

[1]

(ii)   Explain why the magnesium protects the iron from rusting, and how this happens.

....

....

....

[2]

(d)   A coat of zinc could be applied to the iron pipes to prevent them rusting.
What name is given to this method of corrosion protection?

....

[1]

[Total 7 marks]

Turn over ▶

13   The balanced equation below shows what happens when a strip of magnesium metal is dissolved in a solution of hydrochloric acid.

$$Mg_{(s)} + 2HCl_{(aq)} \rightarrow MgCl_{2(aq)} + H_{2(g)}$$

(a)   A student dissolved a piece of magnesium in an excess of hydrochloric acid.
7.50 g of $MgCl_2$ was produced. What mass of magnesium did the student start with?

Mass of magnesium = ... g

[3]

(b)   Describe how the student could test for the gas produced in this reaction, and state what he would observe.

Test ....

....

Observation ....

....

[2]

[Total 5 marks]

14 Soluble salts can be made by reacting an acid with an insoluble base or an alkali.

(a) An excess of zinc oxide is added to a beaker of dilute hydrochloric acid.
The mixture is stirred and the acid is neutralised.

dilute hydrochloric acid

excess of zinc oxide

(i) How could you tell when all the acid has been neutralised?

....

[1]

(ii) Give the products of this reaction.

....

[2]

(b) Describe how you could obtain a pure, dry sample of calcium chloride
from the alkali calcium hydroxide and dilute hydrochloric acid.

....

....

....

....

....

....

[3]

Turn over ▶

(c)   Which **two** substances from the list below could be mixed to obtain calcium sulfate by precipitation? Write the letters of the substances.

A $BaSO_4$

B $CaCl_2$

C $CaCO_3$

D H_2SO_4

Substances .... and ....

[2]

(d)   Complete and balance the chemical equation for the reaction between hydrochloric acid and copper carbonate. Include state symbols.

$CuCO_3$(.......) + ... $\rightarrow$ ....

[3]

[Total 11 marks]

[Total for paper 120 marks]

| Candidate Surname | | Candidate Forename(s) | |

| Centre Number | Candidate Number |

Certificate
International GCSE

Chemistry
Paper 2C

Practice Paper
Time allowed: 1 hour

You must have:
- A ruler.
- A calculator.

Total marks:

Instructions to candidates
- Use **black** ink to write your answers.
- Write your name and other details in the spaces provided above.
- Answer **all** questions in the spaces provided.
- In calculations, show clearly how you worked out your answers.

Information for candidates
- The marks available are given in brackets at the end of each question.
- There are 60 marks available for this paper.
- You might find the periodic table on the inside of the front cover useful.

Advice for candidates
- Read all the questions carefully.
- Write your answers as clearly and neatly as possible.
- Keep in mind how much time you have left.

Answer **all** questions

1   The diagram shows the electronic structures of a sodium atom and a chlorine atom.

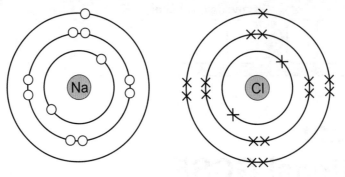

(a)   Chlorine has two major isotopes, ^{35}Cl and ^{37}Cl.

   (i)   State what is meant by the term **isotope**.

   ....

   ....

   [1]

   (ii) ^{35}Cl has a relative abundance of 75%.

         The relative atomic mass of chlorine is 35.5. Show how this value is calculated.

   ....

   ....

   [2]

(b)   Sodium and chlorine react to form the ionic compound sodium chloride.

        Draw a dot and cross diagram of sodium chloride. Show only the outer electrons.

   [3]

(c)   Draw a diagram to show the structure of the ions in a crystal of sodium chloride.
        Include at least four ions of each element in the diagram.

[1]

(d)   Explain why sodium chloride has a high melting point.

....

....

....

[2]

[Total 9 marks]

Turn over ▶

180

2   The Haber process is used to make ammonia from nitrogen and hydrogen.
The chemical equation for the reaction is:

$$N_{2(g)} + 3H_{2(g)} \rightleftharpoons 2NH_{3(g)}$$

(a)   The Haber process reaction reaches a dynamic equilibrium. What does this mean?

....

....

[1]

(b)   Give the temperature at which the Haber process is carried out.

....

[1]

(c)   The reaction between nitrogen and hydrogen is exothermic.

Explain what will happen to the yield of ammonia if the temperature is increased.

....

....

....

[2]

(d)   Give the pressure at which the Haber process is carried out.

....

[1]

(e)   Explain what will happen to the yield of ammonia if the pressure is decreased.

....

....

....

[2]

(f)   What catalyst is used in the Haber process?

....

[1]

(g)   In part of a Haber process reaction vessel, the reaction mixture is cooled to around 30 °C. What does this cooling enable?

....

....

....
                                                                                                                          [2]

(h)   Give **two** uses of the ammonia produced in the Haber process.

Use 1 ....

Use 2 ....
                                                                                                                          [2]
                                                                                                        [Total 12 marks]

Turn over ▶

3   A student investigates the reactions of the Group 1 metals lithium, sodium and potassium, with water. The student's observations are recorded in the table below.

Metal	Observations
lithium	Fizzes, moves across the surface
sodium	Fizzes strongly, melts into a round ball, moves across the surface
potassium	Fizzes violently, melts into a round ball, moves across the surface, a flame is seen

The student decides that the order of reactivity of the three metals is:

- potassium (most reactive)

- sodium

- lithium (least reactive)

(a)   Give **two** pieces of evidence from the table that support the student's conclusion.

1...

....

2...

....

[2]

(b)   Explain the pattern of reactivity that the student has noticed.

....

....

....

....

[2]

(c)   Write a balanced chemical equation for the reaction between lithium and water.

....

[2]

(d)   The student accidentally mixes up some unlabelled samples of lithium chloride and
       potassium chloride. The student decides to do a test to find out which is which,
       using a moistened wire loop. Briefly describe the test that the student could carry out,
       and what the results would be.

       ....PRACTICE.............

       ....

       ....
                                                                                                                              [2]
                                                                                                             [Total 8 marks]

Turn over ▶

4   Hydrogen can be burned in oxygen and used as a fuel.

$$2H_2 + O_2 \rightarrow 2H_2O$$

(a)   Calculate the enthalpy change for the reaction. The bond energy values are given below.

Bond energy values (kJ/mol):

O=O   +498

H–H   +436

O–H   +464

Enthalpy change = ... kJ/mol

[4]

(b)   Is bond breaking an exothermic or endothermic process?

....

[1]

[Total 5 marks]

5 A student is investigating how the rate of the reaction between magnesium strips and hydrochloric acid is affected by the concentration of the acid. The student compares different concentrations of acid by measuring how long it takes for the reaction to produce 20 cm³ of hydrogen gas.

The results of the experiment are shown below.

Concentration of acid (mol/dm³)	Time (s)
0.2	58
0.4	29
0.6	18
0.8	15
1.0	12

(a) Plot the results on the axes below and draw a line of best fit.

[2]

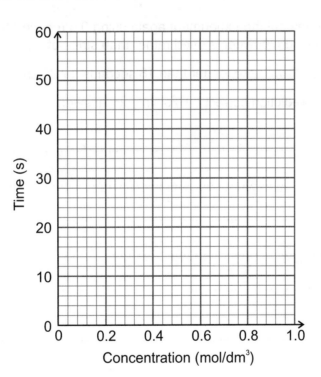

(b) Use your graph to predict the time that it would take for 20 cm³ of hydrogen gas to form with 0.5 mol/dm³ hydrochloric acid.

.... s

[1]

Turn over ▶

(c)   How could the student make his results more reliable?

        ....
                                                                                                                        [1]

(d)   What does the graph show about the effect of concentration on the rate of reaction?

        ....

        ....
                                                                                                                        [1]

(e)   Explain, in terms of collision theory, why concentration affects the rate of a reaction.

        ....

        ....

        ....

        ....
                                                                                                                        [2]

(f)   The student carries out the experiment again using 0.6 mol/dm^3 hydrochloric acid.
        This time, magnesium powder is used rather than strips of metal.

        The student says "it will take longer than 18 seconds for 20 cm^3 of hydrogen gas to form".

        Is the student's prediction correct? Explain your answer.

        ....

        ....

        ....

        ....

        ....
                                                                                                                        [3]
                                                                                                            [Total 10 marks]

6   The diagram shows the repeat unit of an addition polymer.

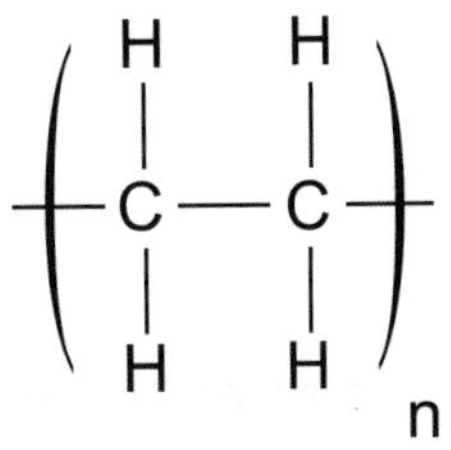

$$\left(\begin{array}{cc} \overset{\displaystyle H}{\underset{\displaystyle H}{\overset{|}{\underset{|}{C}}}} & \overset{\displaystyle H}{\underset{\displaystyle H}{\overset{|}{\underset{|}{C}}}} \end{array}\right)_n$$

(a)   Draw the displayed formula of the monomer used to make this compound.

[1]

(b)   Explain why addition polymers are generally hard to dispose of.

....

....

[1]

(c)   Complete the table below by giving a use for each addition polymer.

[3]

Polymer	Use
poly(ethene)	....
poly(propene)	....
poly(chloroethene)	....

(d)   Some polymers, such as nylon, are not formed by addition polymerisation.

(i)   State the type of polymerisation used to form nylon.

....

[1]

(ii) What is produced along with the polymer during this type of polymerisation reaction?

....

[1]

[Total 7 marks]

Turn over ▶

7 A student is doing an experiment to investigate the electrolysis of sodium chloride solution.

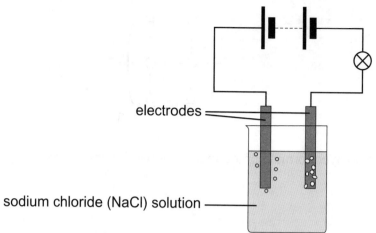

electrodes

sodium chloride (NaCl) solution

(a) Explain why the sodium chloride has to be in solution for electrolysis to occur.

....

....

[2]

(b) Complete the half-equation for the reaction occurring at the positive electrode.

positive electrode .... Cl^- → Cl_2 + ...

[1]

(c) Why is sodium not formed at the negative electrode?

....

....

[1]

(d) What useful product remains in solution?

....

[1]

(e) The student carries out the electrolysis using a current of 4 amps.
Calculate the mass of hydrogen the student would expect to produce after 20 minutes.
(1 faraday = 96000 coulombs.)

The half equation for the reaction at the negative electrode is: $2H^+ + 2e^- → H_2$

Mass of hydrogen = ... g

[4]

[Total 9 marks]

[Total for paper 60 marks]

Pages 7-8

Warm-Up Questions

1) proton and neutron
2) Proton — relative mass = 1, relative charge = +1
   Neutron — relative mass = 1, relative charge = 0
   Electron — relative mass = 1/2000, relative charge = –1
3) Two or more atoms joined together by a covalent bond.

Exam Questions

1 a) strong *(1 mark)*, regular *(1 mark)*, move *(1 mark)*, hotter *(1 mark)*.
   b) E.g. the particles gain energy *(1 mark)*, move around faster *(1 mark)* and go from being close together to being far apart *(1 mark)*.

2 a) D *(1 mark)*
   b) evaporation *(1 mark)*
   c) The particles gain energy *(1 mark)* and vibrate more *(1 mark)*. This weakens the forces that hold the solid together and makes the solid expand *(1 mark)*. At the point of melting, many of the particles have enough energy to break free from their positions *(1 mark)*.

3 a) diffusion *(1 mark)*
   b) D (The water got less purple as the potassium manganate(VII) particles spread further apart.) *(1 mark)*
   c) B (The particles of ammonia are smaller and lighter, so they diffused more quickly.) *(1 mark)*

4 a) element *(1 mark)*
   b) compound *(1 mark)*

Page 15

Warm-Up Questions

1) crystallisation
2) fractional distillation

Exam Questions

1 a) E.g. draw a pencil line near the bottom of a sheet of filter paper and add spots of different inks to the line at intervals *(1 mark)*. Put the paper in a beaker of solvent, e.g. water *(1 mark)*, so that the pencil line and the spots of ink are above the solvent *(1 mark)*.
   b) Printers 1 and 3 could not have produced the document. *(1 mark for both correct)*

2 a) E.g. mix the lawn sand with water to dissolve the ammonium sulfate *(1 mark)*. Filter the mixture using filter paper to remove the sharp sand *(1 mark)*. Pour the remaining solution into an evaporating dish and slowly heat it to evaporate the water *(1 mark)*. Dry the products in a drying oven/desiccator *(1 mark)*.
   b) E.g. the products were not completely dry *(1 mark)*.

3 a) The boiling points of water and methanoic acid are too close together to allow them to be separated by simple distillation *(1 mark)*.
   b)

Temperature on thermometer	Contents of the flask	Contents of the beaker
30 °C	both liquids	no liquid
65 °C	water	propanone
110 °C	no liquid	both liquids

(3 marks available — 1 mark for each correct row.)

   c) The different liquids in the mixture will all have different boiling points *(1 mark)*. When the mixture is heated, the liquid with the lowest boiling point will evaporate first and it will reach the top of the fractionating column when the temperature there matches its boiling point *(1 mark)*. It can then be condensed and collected *(1 mark)*. When the first liquid has been collected, the temperature can be raised until the next liquid evaporates and reaches the top of the column, and so on *(1 mark)*.

Pages 23-24

Warm-Up Questions

1) a) 2
   b) 8
2) reduction
3) positive ions
4) negative ions

Exam Questions

1 a) By atomic number *(1 mark)*
   b) The number of electrons in the outer shell is the same as the group number *(1 mark)*.

2 a) 2, 2 *(1 mark)*
   b)

   (1 mark for the 3rd level correct, 1 mark for the 4th level correct.)

   The important thing here is not where you place the electrons on each energy level ring, but that the number on each level is correct — fill from the inside outward, and remember that you can never have more than two electrons in the first shell, or more than eight in the others.

   c) 2 *(1 mark)*

3 a) Each magnesium atom loses two electrons *(1 mark)* — oxidation *(1 mark)*.
   b) Sulfur atoms have six electrons in their outer shell, so they need two more to make a complete shell of eight electrons *(1 mark)*. Chlorine atoms have seven electrons in their outer shell, so they need one more electron to make a full shell of eight electrons *(1 mark)*.

4 a) strong (large also acceptable) *(1 mark)*, positive *(1 mark)*, negative *(1 mark)*, large *(1 mark)*, high *(1 mark)*.
   b)

   (1 mark for 8 electrons in sodium, 1 mark for 8 electrons in chlorine, 1 mark for both charges correct.)

5 a) Magnesium oxide *(1 mark)* — the 2+ and 2– ions in magnesium oxide attract each other more strongly than the 1+ and 1– ions in sodium chloride *(1 mark)*. The stronger attraction means that more energy will be needed to break the bonds, leading to a higher melting point *(1 mark)*.
   b) i) It has a giant three-dimensional lattice structure *(1 mark)* which is held together by the attraction between the oppositely charged ions *(1 mark)*.

   What's important for the first mark is that it's a giant structure.

   ii) diagram B *(1 mark)*

Page 29

Warm-Up Questions

1) In a covalent bond, the atoms share electrons. In an ionic bond, one of the atoms donates electrons to the other atom.
2) Because the intermolecular forces between the chlorine molecules are very weak.

Exam Questions

1 a) i)   ii)   iii)

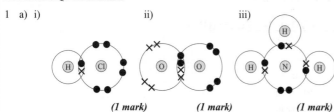

      (1 mark)   *(1 mark)*   *(1 mark)*

b) A pair of electrons (one from the hydrogen atom and one from the chlorine atom) is shared between the two atoms *(1 mark)*. The atoms are held together by the strong attraction between this shared pair and the nuclei of the atoms *(1 mark)*.

2 In a giant covalent structure, all of the atoms are bonded to each other with strong covalent bonds *(1 mark)*. It takes lots of energy to break the many bonds and melt the solid *(1 mark)*.

3 a) In graphite, each carbon atom only forms three covalent bonds, creating layers of carbon atoms *(1 mark)* which can slide over each other, making graphite useful as a lubricant *(1 mark)*.

  b) In diamond, each carbon atom forms four covalent bonds in a very rigid structure *(1 mark)*. This makes diamond very hard, so it is good at cutting other substances *(1 mark)*.

  c) i) B *(1 mark)*

       ii) D *(1 mark)*

Revision Summary for Section 1 — 1 (page 30)

10)   a) 3   b) 2   c) 1   d) 4

11)   a) fractional distillation   b) filtration

16)   2, 8, 8, 1

Pages 37-38

Warm-Up Questions

1) The relative atomic mass.

2) The relative formula mass.

3) percentage yield = (actual yield ÷ theoretical yield) × 100

Exam Questions

1 a) Reactants: methane/CH_4 and oxygen/O_2 *(1 mark)*
     Products: carbon dioxide/CO_2 and water/H_2O *(1 mark)*

  b) methane + oxygen → carbon dioxide + water *(1 mark)*

  c) $CH_4 + 2O_2 \rightarrow CO_2 + 2H_2O$

     (1 mark for the correct reactants and products, 1 mark for correctly balancing the equation)

2 a) Isotopes are different atomic forms of the same element, which have the same number of protons *(1 mark)* but a different number of neutrons *(1 mark)*.

  b)

Isotope	Mass number	Number of protons	Number of neutrons
^{35}Cl	35	17	**18**
^{37}Cl	**37**	17	**20**

     (1 mark for correctly stating the mass number and number of protons in ^{37}Cl, 1 mark for correctly finding the number of neutrons in both ^{35}Cl and ^{37}Cl)

As ^{35}Cl and ^{37}Cl are isotopes of the same element, they must have the same number of protons.

  c) i) The relative atomic mass is the average mass of all the isotopes of an element *(1 mark)* compared with the mass of one atom of carbon-12 *(1 mark)*.

       ii)
$$A_r = \frac{(35 \times 75) + (37 \times 25)}{75 + 25} = \mathbf{35.5}$$

       (1 mark for (35×75)+(37×25), 1 mark for division by 100 (75+25), 1 mark for correct final answer)

In the exam you might see the relative abundances of the isotopes given as percentages (as here), ratios or fractions. It doesn't matter what format the relative abundance numbers are in — you can just multiply them by the relative mass of each isotope and divide by the total of the relative abundances.

3 $Ca(OH)_2 = 40 + (2 \times 16) + (2 \times 1)$ *(1 mark)* = **74** *(1 mark)*

4 Division by A_r: N = 30.4 ÷ 14 = 2.17
   O = 69.6 ÷ 16 = 4.35 *(1 mark)*
   Simplest whole number ratio: 1:2 *(1 mark)*
   Empirical formula: NO_2 *(1 mark)*

5 Calculate the mass of the empirical formula:
   $(3 \times 12) + (7 \times 1) + (16) = 59$ *(1 mark)*
   Divide the relative molecular mass by this mass:
   118 ÷ 59 = 2 *(1 mark)*
   Work out the molecular formula:
   empirical formula × 2 = $C_6H_{14}O_2$ *(1 mark)*

6 a) 2Mg   2MgO
     2 × 24 = 48   2 × (24 + 16) = 80
     48 ÷ 48 = 1 g   80 ÷ 48 = 1.67 g
     1 × 10 = 10 g   1.67 × 10 = **16.7 g**

     (3 marks for correct final answer without any working, otherwise 1 mark for correctly calculating both M_rs and 1 mark for dividing through by 48 and multiplying by 10)

  b) 4Na $2Na_2O$
     4 × 23 = 92   2 × [(2 × 23) + 16] = 124
     92 ÷ 124 = 0.74 g   124 ÷ 124 = 1 g
     0.74 × 2 = 1.48 g   1 × 2 = 2 g

     (3 marks for correct final answer without any working, otherwise 1 mark for correctly calculating both M_rs and 1 mark for dividing through by 124 and multiplying by 2)

7 percentage yield = (6 ÷ 15) × 100 = **40%** *(1 mark)*

8 A = (3.18 ÷ 3.33) × 100 = **95.5%**
   B = (3.05 ÷ 3.33) × 100 = **91.6%**
   C = (3.15 ÷ 3.33) × 100 = **94.6%**

   (3 marks available — 1 mark for each correct percentage yield)

Pages 44-45

Warm-Up Questions

1)   56 g

2)   Avogadro's number / the Avogadro constant

Exam Questions

1 a)
$$\text{number of moles} = \frac{\text{mass in grams}}{M_r}$$ *(1 mark)*

  b) i)   14 ÷ 7 = **2 moles** *(1 mark)*
      ii)   112 ÷ 32 = **3.5 moles** *(1 mark)*
      iii)   390 ÷ (28 + (16 × 2)) = **6.5 moles** *(1 mark)*
      iv)   275 ÷ (65 + 12 + (16 × 3)) = **2.2 moles** *(1 mark)*

  c) i)   59 g *(1 mark)*
      ii)   2 × 27 = **54 g** *(1 mark)*
      iii)   6 × (1 + 35.5) = **219 g** *(1 mark)*
      iv)   4.5 × (63.5 + 16) = **357.75 g** *(1 mark)*

2 a) 2.5 × 0.125 = 0.3125 moles *(1 mark)*

  b) 3 ÷ 0.75 = 4 mol/dm^3 *(1 mark)*

  c) M_r of Na_2SO_4 = (23 × 2) + 32 + (16 × 4) = 142 *(1 mark)*
     Mass = 4 × 142 = 568 g

     Concentration in g/dm^3 = **568 g/dm^3** *(1 mark)*

3   Mass of 4 moles of KOH = $4 \times 56 = 224$ g *(1 mark)*

Extra mass needed = $224 - 140 =$ **84 g** *(1 mark)*

4 a) E.g. to remove all of the water from the salt *(1 mark)*.

    b) i) $61.224 - 53.500 =$ **7.724 g** *(1 mark)*

        ii) $56.364 - 53.500 =$ **2.864 g** *(1 mark)*

    c) M_r of $Na_2CO_3 = (23 \times 2) + 12 + (16 \times 3) = 106$ *(1 mark)*

Moles of water lost:

Mass of water lost = $7.724 - 2.864 = 4.86$ g

Moles of water lost = $4.86 \div 18 = 0.27$ moles *(1 mark)*

Moles of anhydrous salt produced:

Moles of $Na_2CO_3 = 2.864 \div 106 = 0.027$ moles *(1 mark)*

Ratio of salt to water:

0.027 moles of salt (Na_2CO_3) : 0.27 moles of water

1 mole of Na_2CO_3 : $(0.27 \div 0.027) = 10$ moles of water

x = **10** *(1 mark)*

5 a) 24 dm³ / 24 000 cm³ *(1 mark)*

    b) i) $1.5 \times 24 =$ **36 dm³** *(1 mark)*

        ii) $2.25 \div 24 = 0.094$ moles OR $2250 \div 24\,000 = 0.094$ moles

           (1 mark)

    c) C CO_2

       12   44

       $12 \div 12 = 1$ $44 \div 12 = 3.667$ *(1 mark)*

       $1 \times 6.9 = 6.9$ g $3.667 \times 6.9 = 25.3$ g

So 6.9 g of C gives 25.3 g of CO_2 *(1 mark)*.

Volume = $(25.3 \div 44) \times 24$ *(1 mark)* = **13.8 dm³** *(1 mark)*

Pages 53-54

Warm-Up Questions

1)   electrolysis

2)   It must be molten or dissolved in water.

3)   the cathode

Exam Questions

1 a)

State	Conducts electricity? (yes/no)
Solid	No *(1 mark)*
Dissolved in water	Yes *(1 mark)*
Molten	Yes *(1 mark)*

    b) When it is molten or in solution it conducts electricity because the ions separate and are free to move about *(1 mark)*, so they can carry electric current. When it is solid it doesn't conduct electricity because the ions are held rigidly and aren't free to move and carry electric current *(1 mark)*.

    c) Electric current is a flow of electrons or ions *(1 mark)*.

    d) E.g. covalent compounds make bonds by sharing electrons so they don't contain ions *(1 mark)*. This means that they don't have any charge carriers that are free to move and carry an electric current *(1 mark)*.

2 a) E.g. metals have a giant structure of positive ions surrounded by a sea of delocalised electrons *(1 mark)*.

    b) E.g. metals are good conductors of electricity because the free electrons in the structure carry electrical current *(1 mark)*. Most metals are malleable because the layers of atoms in metals can slide over each other, allowing them to be hammered or rolled into sheets *(1 mark)*.

3 a) i)   Product = H_2/hydrogen, State = gas

           (1 mark for product, 1 mark for state)

        ii) Product = Cl_2/chlorine, State = gas

           (1 mark for product, 1 mark for state)

    b) E.g. the metal ion, sodium (Na^+), is more reactive than the hydrogen ion (H^+) / hydrogen ions accept electrons more easily than sodium ions *(1 mark)*.

4 a) Pb^{2+}: **A**, molten lead: **C**, Br^-: **B**, Br_2: **D** *(2 marks for all letters correct, 1 mark for 2 or more letters correct)*

    b) $Pb^{2+} + 2e^- \rightarrow Pb$

       (1 mark for correct equation, 1 mark for correct balancing)

    c) $2Br^- \rightarrow Br_2 + 2e^-$

       (1 mark for correct equation, 1 mark for correct balancing)

    d) i)   electrolytes *(1 mark)*

        ii) E.g. you can place a conductivity probe into the substance *(1 mark)*. If a reading of zero conductivity is shown, the substance is a non-electrolyte *(1 mark)*. / You can set up an electrolytic cell *(1 mark)* and if the substance undergoes electrolysis then it is an electrolyte *(1 mark)*.

        iii) It could be melted *(1 mark)*.

5 a) $0.2 \times (40 \times 60) = 480$ C *(1 mark)*

      $480 \div 96\,000 =$ **0.005 F** *(1 mark)*

    b) 0.005 mol *(1 mark)*

To get this answer you need to divide the number of faradays by the number of electrons in the half-equation. Here you divide by 1, which is why the answer is the same as the number of faradays.

    c) M_r of silver = 108. 108×0.005 *(1 mark)* = **0.54 g** *(1 mark)*

Revision Summary for Section 1 — 2 (page 55)

2) a) $2Na + 2H_2O \rightarrow 2NaOH + H_2$

    b) $2Al + 6HCl \rightarrow 2AlCl_3 + 3H_2$

3) 20.18

4) a) 98   b) 125   c) 82   d) 72

5) Ca: $227 \div 40 = 5.68$

    F: $216 \div 19 = 11.37$

    Divide both by 5.68 to get a ratio of 1:2.

    So, the empirical formula is CaF_2.

6) empirical mass = $(2 \times 12) + (5 \times 1) + 35.5 = 64.5$

    number of empirical units in the molecule

    = $258 \div 64.5 = 4$ empirical units

    $C_2H_5Cl \times 4 = C_8H_{20}Cl_4$

7) a) $4Na + O_2 \rightarrow 2Na_2O$

      4Na: $4 \times 23 = 92$

      $2Na_2O$: $((23 \times 2) + 16) \times 2) = 124$

      Na Na_2O

      92 g   124 g

      1 g   1.348 g

      50 g   **67.4 g** (to 1 d.p.)

    b) Percentage yield = $42.3 \div 67.4 \times 100 = 62.8\%$ (to 1 d.p.)

8) moles = mass $\div M_r = 147 \div (23 + 16 + 1)$

                = $147 \div 40 = 3.7$ moles (to 1 d.p.)

9) mass = moles $\times M_r = 0.05 \times (24 + 16)$

              = $0.05 \times 40 = 2$ g

10) mass of $FeCl_2.XH_2O = 28.133 - 23.299 = 4.834$ g

    mass of $FeCl_2 = 26.347 - 23.299 = 3.048$ g

    mass of H_2O lost = $4.834 - 3.048 = 1.786$ g

    moles H_2O lost = $1.786 \div 18 = 0.0992$

    M_r of $FeCl_2 = 56 + (35.5 \times 2) = 127$ g/mol

    moles of $FeCl_2$ in 3.048 g = 3.048 g $\div 127$ g/mol = 0.024 moles

    X = $0.0992 \div 0.024 = 4.13 \approx 4$

    So, the formula of the hydrated salt is $FeCl_2.4H_2O$.

11) volume = moles $\times 24 = 88.8$ dm³

12) moles = concentration $\times$ volume

          = $2 \times (250 \div 1000) = 0.5$ moles

13) concentration = moles $\div$ volume

           = $0.55 \div (500 \div 1000)$

           = $0.55 \div 0.5 = 1.1$ mol/dm³

18) $Pb^{2+} + 2e^- \rightarrow Pb$

charge = current × time = 7200 C

faradays = 7200 ÷ 96 000 = 0.075 F

moles of product $\quad$ = 0.075 ÷ 2 (electrons)
$\qquad\qquad\qquad$ = 0.0375 moles of Pb atoms

mass Pb = M_r × moles = 207 × 0.0375 = 7.76 g (to 2 d.p.)

Pages 62-63
Warm-Up Questions
1) A metal oxide. All metal oxides have a pH higher than 7 when they form a solution/are basic. (Non-metal oxides have a pH less than 7 in solution/are acidic.)
2) Na and K are in the same group so they have the same number of electrons in their outer shell.
3) They have a full outer shell of electrons so they don't need to lose or gain electrons in a reaction to obtain a full outer shell.
4) Oxidation is the loss of electrons. Reduction is the gain of electrons.

Exam Questions
1 a) a period *(1 mark)*
   b) The two elements will have similar properties *(1 mark)*
   c) To the right of the line *(1 mark)*. Since it does not conduct electricity, it must be a non-metal *(1 mark)*.
2 a) Metal B is the most reactive *(1 mark)* because it takes the least time to react completely with the water *(1 mark)*.
   b) A = sodium, B = potassium and C = lithium.
   (2 marks for all three answers correct, otherwise 1 mark for any one answer correct.)
   c) sodium hydroxide *(1 mark)*, hydrogen *(1 mark)*
   d) Rubidium is further down the group than potassium/metal B *(1 mark)*, so it is more reactive/will take less time to react *(1 mark)*.
   e) As you go down Group 1, the outer electron is further from the nucleus *(1 mark)*, which means it is less strongly attracted to the nucleus *(1 mark)*. So as you go down Group 1 the outer electron is more easily lost *(1 mark)*.
3 a) Chlorine — green *(1 mark)*
   Iodine — solid *(1 mark)*
   b) i) Fluorine is more reactive than chlorine *(1 mark)*.
      ii) gas *(1 mark)*
4 a) $H_{2(g)} + Cl_{2(g)} \rightarrow 2HCl_{(g)}$
   (1 mark for the correct reactants and products, 1 mark for balancing the equation, 1 mark for correct state symbols.)
   b) i) When hydrogen chloride is dissolved in water the molecules dissociate into H^+ ions and Cl^- ions *(1 mark)*. The H^+ ions make the solution acidic *(1 mark)*. When hydrogen chloride is dissolved in methylbenzene, it doesn't dissociate *(1 mark)*. There are no H^+ ions produced, so it's not acidic *(1 mark)*.
      ii) hydrochloric acid *(1 mark)*
5 a) A displacement reaction is where a more reactive element displaces a less reactive element from a compound *(1 mark)*.
   b) i) $Br_2 + 2KI \rightarrow I_2 + 2KBr$
      (1 mark for the correct reactants and products, 1 mark for balancing the equation.)
      ii) E.g. Bromine is more reactive than iodine *(1 mark)*, so it will displace the iodine from the potassium iodide *(1 mark)*.
   c) i) A reaction where reduction and oxidation happen at the same time, and so one substance loses electrons and another substance gains electrons *(1 mark)*.
      ii) Bromine *(1 mark)*.
   Bromine goes from Br_2 to Br^- ions (in potassium bromide) during this reaction. This means that the bromine is accepting electrons from the iodine ions and being reduced — so it must be the oxidising agent.
6 Before — colourless *(1 mark)*
   After — orange *(1 mark)*

Pages 68-69
Warm-Up Questions
1) magnesium chloride
2) calcium
3) Because the more reactive metal will bind more strongly to oxygen than the less reactive metal.
4) oxygen, water

Exam Questions
1 a) least vigorous $B \rightarrow A \rightarrow C \rightarrow D$ most vigorous
   (1 mark for two letters in the correct places in the order, 2 marks for all four letters in the correct places in the order.)
   The clue is in the diagrams — the reaction that produces the most gas will push the gas syringe out the furthest.
   b) zinc *(1 mark)*
2 a) iron / tin / lead *(1 mark)*
   The unidentified metal must be more reactive than copper (as it displaces copper from copper sulfate), but less reactive than zinc (which it doesn't displace from zinc sulfate).
   b) The copper was displaced from its salt *(1 mark)*.
3 a) tube B *(1 mark)*
   b) The addition of oxygen / the loss of electrons *(1 mark)*.
   c) The painted nail would not rust *(1 mark)*, because the paint creates a barrier that keeps out water and oxygen *(1 mark)*.
   d) i) galvanising *(1 mark)*
      ii) Zinc is more reactive than iron *(1 mark)*, so the zinc will be oxidised instead of the iron *(1 mark)*.
   e) oiling *(1 mark)*
4 a) The result for the reaction between aluminium and aluminium oxide *(1 mark)*. The result for the reaction between magnesium and iron oxide *(1 mark)*.
   b) none *(1 mark)*
   c) Metal: magnesium *(1 mark)*
   Reason: it is the most reactive metal in the table *(1 mark)*.

Pages 76-78
Warm-Up Questions
1) a) 78%
   b) 21%
   c) 0.04%
2) Soak some iron wool in acetic acid. Push the wool into a test tube, put your thumb over the end and invert the tube into a beaker of water. Over time, the level of water in the test tube will rise. To work out the percentage of the air that is oxygen, mark the starting and finishing positions of the water. Then, fill the tube up to each mark with water and pour the contents into a measuring cylinder to find out the volume of air at the start and end. Use the difference between the start and end volumes to work out the percentage of the starting volume that has been used up.
3) A downward delivery system
4) $CaCO_3 + 2HCl \rightarrow CaCl_2 + H_2O + CO_2$

Exam Questions
1 Dry air is 21% oxygen
100% − 21% = 79%
50 cm³ × 0.79 = **39.5 cm³**
(accept 20-22% oxygen and a correctly calculated volume)
(2 marks for correct answer, otherwise 1 mark for using any correct method)

2

Element	Flame colour when burnt	Oxide formed	Acid-base character of oxide
sodium	Yellow-orange	Na_2O	Alkaline
magnesium	White	MgO	Slightly alkaline
carbon	Orange/yellow	CO_2	Slightly acidic
sulfur	Blue	SO_2	Acidic

(1 mark for each correct answer)

3 a) $2H_2O_{2(aq)} \rightarrow 2H_2O_{(l)} + O_{2(g)}$
(1 mark for correct formulas of reactant and products including their state symbols, 1 mark for correctly balancing the equation.)

You'd still get the marks for any multiple of the balanced equation in a question like this (for example $H_2O_{2(aq)} \rightarrow H_2O_{(l)} + \frac{1}{2}O_{2(g)}$).

   b) i)   17 cm³ *(1 mark)*

      ii) Any one from: e.g. use a delivery tube to bubble gas into an upside-down measuring cylinder filled with water. / Use a gas syringe. *(1 mark)*

      iii) Manganese(IV) oxide was the most effective catalyst *(1 mark)* because it led to the greatest volume of oxygen being produced over the time period measured/increased the rate of reaction by the greatest amount *(1 mark)*.

4 a)   E.g. the delivery tube needs to feed downwards into an upright test tube *(1 mark)*. Carbon dioxide is more dense than air, so it will displace the air and collect in the tube/it cannot be collected in an upside-down test tube *(1 mark)*.

You can have the first mark here for any other sensible suggestion, like swapping the test tube for a gas syringe.

   b) copper oxide *(1 mark)*

   c) thermal decomposition *(1 mark)*

5 a) i)   Carbon dioxide is **slightly** *(1 mark)* soluble in water. The bubbling when a fizzy drink bottle is opened is carbon dioxide escaping from the drink when the pressure is **released** *(1 mark)*.

      ii) Carbon dioxide is **denser** *(1 mark)* than air. It is used in some fire extinguishers. It stops the **oxygen** *(1 mark)* that the fire needs getting to the flames.

   b) Heat detector B *(1 mark)*, e.g. because the nitrogen will absorb less heat than the carbon dioxide/the carbon dioxide will absorb more heat than the nitrogen *(1 mark)*.

   c) Carbon dioxide absorbs heat that would otherwise be radiated out into space *(1 mark)* and re-radiates some of it back towards the Earth *(1 mark)*.

   d) i)   The temperature increased *(1 mark)*.

      ii) E.g. climate change / changing rainfall patterns / sea level rise / flooding *(1 mark)*

Be careful — you can't say 'global warming' here because that's just an alternative name for the temperature change, not an effect of it.

Pages 83-84
Warm-Up Questions

1) lithium

2) a)   Use a piece of red litmus paper which has been dampened. If there's ammonia present, the litmus paper will turn blue.

   b)   You can add some sodium hydroxide to the substance and then test for ammonia. If ammonia is given off, there are ammonium ions in the substance.

3) Use a piece of damp litmus paper. If chlorine is present it will bleach the paper, turning it white.

4) blue

Exam Questions

1 a)   E.g. take a clean platinum wire loop, dip it into the substance to be tested and put the material into the hot part of a Bunsen burner flame.
(1 mark for any suitable method stated to transfer the material into the flame, 1 mark for saying that the material needs to be placed in the flame)

   b) Potassium would give a lilac flame *(1 mark)* but sodium would give a yellow-orange flame *(1 mark)*.

   c) The medicines also contain sodium ions *(1 mark)*, so the colour produced by the sodium could interfere with the flame test result *(1 mark)*.

2 a) i)   dilute hydrochloric acid *(1 mark)*, barium chloride solution *(1 mark)*

      ii) a white precipitate *(1 mark)*

   b) i)   e.g. dilute hydrochloric acid *(1 mark)*

Any dilute acid will do here — you'd usually use hydrochloric, but sulfuric or nitric would work too.

      ii) carbon dioxide *(1 mark)*

   c) Add dilute nitric acid *(1 mark)* followed by silver nitrate solution *(1 mark)*. Chloride ions will give a white precipitate *(1 mark)* whereas bromide ions will give a cream precipitate *(1 mark)*.

3 a)

Metal ion	Colour of precipitate
Fe^{2+}	green
Cu^{2+}	blue
Fe^{3+}	reddish brown

(1 mark for each ion or colour)

   b) $Fe^{2+}_{(aq)} + 2OH^-_{(aq)} \rightarrow Fe(OH)_{2(s)}$ *(1 mark)*

   c) $Fe^{3+}_{(aq)} + 3OH^-_{(aq)} \rightarrow Fe(OH)_{3(s)}$
(1 mark for the reactants and product, 1 mark for the state symbols, 1 mark for balancing the equation.)

4 a)   Test the gas with a lighted splint *(1 mark)*. Hydrogen will burn with a squeaky pop *(1 mark)*.

   b) Test the gas with a glowing splint *(1 mark)*. Oxygen will relight it *(1 mark)*.

5 a) i)   white *(1 mark)*

      ii) The white powder would turn blue *(1 mark)*.

   b) Pure water has a boiling point of 100 °C *(1 mark)* and a freezing point of 0 °C *(1 mark)*, so the liquid cannot be pure water *(1 mark)*.

   c) Chlorine gas bleaches damp litmus paper *(1 mark)*.
Carbon dioxide gas turns limewater cloudy *(1 mark)*.
So the gas does contain carbon dioxide *(1 mark)* but it doesn't contain chlorine *(1 mark)*.

Revision Summary for Section 2
(page 85)

18) Magnesium displaces copper to form magnesium oxide.

19) The aluminium will displace the zinc to form aluminium sulfate.

Pages 93-94

Warm-Up Questions

1) methane, ethane, propane, butane, pentane

2) When there's plenty of oxygen.

3) C_nH_{2n}

4) They contain carbon-carbon double bonds.

5) The C=C bond can split, allowing a halogen atom to be added to each of the carbons.

6) The bromine water will go colourless.

7) Using ethene and steam / fermentation of sugars.

194

Exam Questions

1 (a) A hydrocarbon is a molecule/compound that is made up of hydrogen and carbon atoms *(1 mark)* only *(1 mark)*.

(b) (i) C_nH_{2n+2} *(1 mark)*

A general formula means you can replace the 'n's with a number to get the formula of a certain molecule in the series — so the 4th alkane is $C_4H_{(2\times4+2)} = C_4H_{10}$.

(ii) homologous series *(1 mark)*

(c)

H—C—C—C—C—H (with H atoms) *(1 mark)*

(d) methane + bromine $\xrightarrow{UV}$ bromomethane + hydrogen bromide
(1 mark for each correct product)

It doesn't matter which way round you write the two missing answers here.

2 (a) E.g. in a saturated molecule all of the atoms are bonded to as many other atoms as they can be / all of the bonds are single covalent bonds *(1 mark)*.

(b) (i) $2C_4H_{10} + 13O_2 \rightarrow 8CO_2 + 10H_2O$
(1 mark for formulas of all reactants and products correct, 1 mark for equation being correctly balanced)

(ii) carbon monoxide *(1 mark)*, carbon *(1 mark)*

3

Name of alkene	Formula	Displayed formula
Ethene	C_2H_4	H₂C=CH₂
Propene	C_3H_6	H₂C=CH–CH₃

(4 marks available — 1 mark for each correct name or formula)

The displayed formula for propene could also be drawn with the double bond between the second and third carbon atoms. As long as you've got the right number of hydrogen atoms attached to each carbon atom, it doesn't matter which two carbons the double bond is between.

4 (a) $C_2H_5OH \rightarrow C_2H_4 + H_2O$ *(1 mark)*

(b) a dehydration reaction *(1 mark)*

(c) aluminium oxide *(1 mark)*

5 (a)

Method	Reaction	Temperature needed
A	$C_2H_4 + \mathbf{H_2O} \rightarrow C_2H_5OH$	300 °C
B	$C_6H_{12}O_6 \rightarrow 2CO_2 + \mathbf{2}C_2H_5OH$	about 30 °C

(4 marks available — 1 mark for each reaction or temperature)

(b) fermentation *(1 mark)*

(c) Pressure — 60-70 atmospheres *(1 mark)*
Catalyst — phosphoric acid *(1 mark)*

(d) Method A *(1 mark)* — crude oil is the raw material from which ethene is made, and there is a good supply for country Z. / If country Z has a very cold climate, sugar cane probably won't grow well, and this is the raw material for method B *(1 mark)*.

Pages 101-102

Warm-Up Questions

1) 0-14

2) neutral

3) pH 13/14

4) sulfuric acid + magnesium oxide → magnesium sulfate + water

5) E.g. phenolphthalein / methyl orange

Exam Questions

1

Indicator	Colour
Litmus paper	blue
Phenolphthalein	pink
Universal indicator	purple
Methyl orange	yellow

(3 marks for whole table correct, otherwise 1 mark for each correct answer)

2 a) H^+ ions/hydrogen ions *(1 mark)*

b) neutralisation *(1 mark)*

c) The solution will turn green (because universal indicator is green in neutral solutions) *(1 mark)*.

3 a) carbon dioxide *(1 mark)*

Don't just give the formula of carbon dioxide — the question asks you to name the gas.

b) $2HNO_3 + CaCO_3 \rightarrow Ca(NO_3)_2 + H_2O + CO_2$ *(1 mark for the correct formulae, 1 mark for correct balancing)*

c) hydrochloric acid *(1 mark)*

4 a) A — calcium nitrate *(1 mark)*, D — potassium sulfate *(1 mark)*

b) Filter the mixture (to separate the solid calcium sulfate from the liquid) *(1 mark)*.

5 a) soluble *(1 mark)*

b) acids *(1 mark)*

c) insoluble *(1 mark)*, sodium *(1 mark)*

6 a) Any one from: the excess of silver carbonate will sink to the bottom of the flask and stay there / the mixture will stop producing bubbles (of carbon dioxide) *(1 mark)*.

b) silver carbonate + nitric acid → silver nitrate + water + carbon dioxide *(1 mark)*

c) filtration *(1 mark)*

d) Evaporate off the water *(1 mark)*.

e) i) Potassium hydroxide is soluble, so you can't tell/see when the reaction is finished *(1 mark)*. This means you can't add an excess of solid to the acid and filter out what's left *(1 mark)*.

ii) E.g. work out exactly how much potassium hydroxide is needed to neutralise the nitric acid by gradually measuring out the alkali into a known volume of the acid *(1 mark)* and using an indicator to show when the reaction has finished/neutralisation has occurred *(1 mark)*. Repeat the reaction using exactly the same volumes of acid and alkali, but no indicator, to produce the pure solution *(1 mark)*.

Pages 112-114

Warm-Up Questions

1) E.g. the corrosion of iron is a reaction that happens very slowly. Explosions are very fast reactions.

2) Any three of, e.g. increase the temperature (of the acid). / Use smaller pieces of/powdered magnesium. / Increase the acid concentration. / Use a catalyst.

3) E.g. observe a mark through the solution and measure how long it takes for it to disappear.

4) E.g. measure the volume of gas given off by collecting it in a gas syringe / monitor the mass of a reaction flask from which the gas escapes.

5) Solid catalysts give the reacting particles a surface to stick to. They increase the number of successful collisions by lowering the activation energy.

Exam Questions

1 a) A *(1 mark)*

b) Curve C, as below. The curve should be between curves A and B *(1 mark)*.

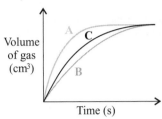

Volume of gas (cm³)

Time (s)

c) i) E.g. the teacher would have used the same volume / concentration of acid in each experiment *(1 mark)*. This variable is controlled so that you can tell if the variable you're changing is causing the results *(1 mark)*.

ii) E.g. yes *(1 mark)*, because the same volume of gas was produced in each experiment *(1 mark)*.

This suggests that either the same volume of acid, or an excess of acid, was used in both experiments.

d) A — Measuring how quickly the reaction loses mass *(1 mark)*.

2 a)

Average volume of gas produced (cm³)
94
64
45.5
19.5
9

(1 mark for at least 3 values correct, 2 marks for all 5 values correct)

b) i) 2 mol/dm³ *(1 mark)*

ii) It produced the largest volume of gas in the given time *(1 mark)*.

c) i) Gas syringe *(1 mark)*

ii) Any one from: stopwatch (accept e.g. stopclock/timer) / balance / measuring cylinder (or equivalent, e.g. burette) *(1 mark)*

d) To improve the reliability of his results *(1 mark)*.

3 a) R *(1 mark)*. It has the steepest graph and flattens off soonest, so it is the fastest reaction *(1 mark)*.

b) E.g. temperature / the volume/mass of H_2O_2 / the concentration of H_2O_2 *(1 mark)*.

4 a) Increasing the pressure means there are more particles/molecules/atoms of gas in a given volume/space / the particles are closer together *(1 mark)* so collisions happen more frequently *(1 mark)*.

b) i) activation energy *(1 mark)*

ii) By increasing the temperature *(1 mark)*.

5 a) i) The one that uses powdered magnesium carbonate *(1 mark)*.

ii) The powdered magnesium carbonate has a larger surface area *(1 mark)*. This means the particles will collide with it more often/ more frequently *(1 mark)*.

b) A lower concentration would have fewer reactant particles in a certain volume. / The particles would be further apart in a lower concentration *(1 mark)*. This means that particles would collide less frequently *(1 mark)*.

Pages 118-119

Warm-Up Questions

1) An exothermic reaction is one which gives out energy to the surroundings, usually in the form of heat and usually shown by a rise in temperature.

2) An endothermic reaction is one which takes in energy from the surroundings, usually in the form of heat and usually shown by a fall in temperature.

3) When bonds are formed.

Exam Questions

1 a) Endothermic *(1 mark)*. The temperature decrease shows that the reaction is taking in energy from the surroundings *(1 mark)*.

b) A–B *(1 mark)*, because the reaction is endothermic and so more heat energy is taken in when this bond is broken than is released when the A–C bond is formed *(1 mark)*.

c) i) The overall change in energy during a reaction *(1 mark)*.

ii) positive *(1 mark)*

iii) ΔH *(1 mark)*

2 a) endothermic *(1 mark)*

b) The minimum energy needed by reacting particles for a reaction to occur *(1 mark)*.

c) They provide a different pathway with a lower activation energy *(1 mark)*.

3 a) Endothermic *(1 mark)* because it requires heating/takes in energy from the surroundings / because the reverse reaction is favoured by a lower temperature *(1 mark)*.

b) negative *(1 mark)*

4 a) i) A / C / D *(1 mark)*

ii) B / E *(1 mark)*

iii) C *(1 mark)*

iv) B *(1 mark)*

b) i) –90 kJ/mol *(1 mark)*

ii) 70 kJ/mol *(1 mark)*

iii) The curve should start and end at the same energy level as the original curve (grey), but have a lower peak/activation energy *(1 mark)*.

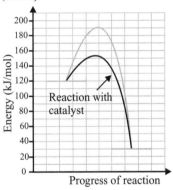

Reaction with catalyst

Energy (kJ/mol)

Progress of reaction

5 (4 × 412) + (2 × 498) = 2644 kJ/mol *(1 mark)*
(2 × 743) + (4 × 463) = 3338 kJ/mol *(1 mark)*
Enthalpy change = 2644 – 3338 = **–694 kJ/mol** *(1 mark for correct value, 1 mark for correct sign)*

Pages 124-125

Warm-Up Questions

1) To reduce the amount of energy lost to the surroundings.

2) The amount of energy needed to raise the temperature of 1 gram of water by 1 °C.

3) It means the relative (%) quantities of reactants and products will reach a certain balance and stay there.

4) The equilibrium will move to the right/towards products.

5) The equilibrium will move to the left/towards reactants.

6) It would have no effect (because there are equal numbers of gas molecules on both sides).

Exam Questions

1 a) Because copper conducts heat very well *(1 mark)*.

b) heat energy change = 50 × 4.2 × 30.5 = **6405 J** *(1 mark)*

c) Energy produced = 6405 ÷ 0.7 *(1 mark)*
= 9150 J/g = **9.15 kJ/g** *(1 mark)*

2 a) M_r of ethanol = $(2 \times 12) + (6 \times 1) + (1 \times 16) = 46$ *(1 mark)*
       Number of moles = $1.15 \div 46 = $ **0.025** *(1 mark)*

   b) Molar enthalpy change = $-7.245 \div 0.025$ *(1 mark)*
       = **−289.8 kJ/mol** *(1 mark)*

The enthalpy change (−7.245 kJ) is negative because combustion is an exothermic reaction.

3 a) It is reversible *(1 mark)*.

   b) Both (the forward and reverse) reactions are taking place *(1 mark)* at exactly the same rate *(1 mark)*.

   c) i)   It takes in heat *(1 mark)*, because it's endothermic/all reversible reactions are exothermic in one direction and endothermic in the other direction. *(1 mark)*

       ii) One reaction is always exothermic and the other endothermic *(1 mark)*, so a change in temperature will always favour one reaction more than the other *(1 mark)*.

       iii) left *(1 mark)*

   d) It won't affect the position of equilibrium *(1 mark)*, because there are the same number of molecules on either side of the equation *(1 mark)*.

Make sure you talk about the number of moles/molecules in your answer — if you only mention volume you won't get the mark.

   e) It is not a closed system / the products can escape *(1 mark)*.

4 a) Endothermic *(1 mark)*, because it is favoured by heating/heat is taken in *(1 mark)*.

   b) i)   It turns from white to blue *(1 mark)*.

       ii) It increases *(1 mark)*.

Revision Summary for Section 4 (page 126)

4) $2HCl + ZnCO_3 \rightarrow ZnCl_2 + H_2O + CO_2$

8) Number of moles of NaOH
    = concentration × volume = $0.25 \times (25/1000) = 0.00625$

    Equation: $NaOH + HCl \rightarrow NaCl + H_2O$

    There's one mole of NaOH to every mole of HCl, so 0.00625 moles of HCl were used.

    Concentration of HCl
    = $0.00625 \div (42/1000) = 0.15$ moles per dm^3

11) b)

15) a) Bonds broken:
        2 moles of H–H bonds = $2 \times 436 = 872$ kJ
        1 mole of O=O bonds = 496 kJ
        Total energy needed to break bonds = $872 + 496 = 1368$ kJ

        Bonds made:
        2 moles of (2 × O–H bonds) = $2 \times 2 \times 463 = 1852$ kJ
        So enthalpy change (ΔH) = $1368 - 1852 = -484$ kJ/mol.

    b) This is an exothermic reaction.

16) a) Mass of water heated = $116 \text{ g} - 64 \text{ g} = 52$ g
        Temperature rise of water = $47 \,°C - 17 \,°C = 30 \,°C$
        Mass of pentane burnt = $97.72 \text{ g} - 97.37 \text{ g} = 0.35$ g

        So 0.35 g of pentane provides enough energy to heat up 52 g of water by 30 °C.

        It takes 4.2 joules of energy to heat up 1 g of water by 1 °C.

        Therefore, the energy produced in this experiment is $4.2 \times 52 \times 30 = 6552$ joules.

        So, 0.35 g of pentane produces 6552 joules of energy, meaning 1 g of pentane produces $6552/0.35 = 18\,720$ J or 18.72 kJ

Pages 133-134

Warm-Up Questions

1) Heat it with carbon monoxide (or with carbon and oxygen).

2) aluminium oxide

3) haematite/Fe_2O_3

4) calcium silicate/$CaSiO_3$
    It is formed in a blast furnace when limestone is decomposed by heat into calcium oxide and CO_2. The calcium oxide then reacts with sand/sodium silicate to form slag.

Exam Questions

1 a) electrolysis *(1 mark)*

   b) If the metal is more reactive than carbon, it can't be extracted using carbon *(1 mark)*.

2 a) i)   The cost of electricity / a lot of electricity is needed *(1 mark)*.

       ii) It reduces the temperature needed to carry out the electrolysis *(1 mark)*, which makes the process cheaper to run *(1 mark)*.

   b) $Al^{3+} + 3e^- \rightarrow Al$
       $2O^{2-} \rightarrow O_2 + 4e^-$
       (3 marks available — 1 mark for correct aluminium equation, 1 mark for correct oxygen equation, 1 mark for correct balancing of both equations)

   c) They are reduced *(1 mark)*, because they gain electrons *(1 mark)*.

   d) The positive electrode *(1 mark)*, because it is getting constantly worn down by reacting with the oxygen that is produced at that electrode *(1 mark)*

3 a) Any three from: e.g. they are both lustrous / both have high tensile strength/are strong / are both malleable / are both good conductors of electricity / are both good conductors of heat *(Maximum of 3 marks available — 1 mark for each property)*.

   b) E.g. aluminium is much less dense than iron, which means aeroplanes can be made lighter and therefore more efficient / unlike iron, aluminium doesn't corrode, which is important as the aeroplane will come into contact with water if it rains *(1 mark)*.

4 a) Steel *(1 mark)*. It has very good malleability so it can be shaped easily *(1 mark)*.

   b) E.g. it is resistant to corrosion/doesn't rust *(1 mark)*.

5 a) i) $C + O_2 \rightarrow CO_2$ *(1 mark)*
            $CO_2 + C \rightarrow 2CO$ *(1 mark)*

       ii) The coke burns and produces carbon dioxide/CO_2 *(1 mark)*. The carbon dioxide/CO_2 then reacts with unburnt coke to produce carbon monoxide/CO *(1 mark)*.

   b) i) $3CO + Fe_2O_3 \rightarrow 3CO_2 + 2Fe$
            (2 marks available — 1 mark for the correct reactants and products, 1 mark for correctly balancing the equation)

       ii) reduced *(1 mark)*

Pages 140-142

Warm-Up Questions

1) 600 °C – 700 °C

2) Addition polymers are made when monomers with a carbon-carbon double bond (alkenes) join together under high pressure and in the presence of a catalyst.

3) E.g. packaging / plastic bags / plastic bottles / plastic containers

Exam Questions

1 a) Carbon monoxide can form if the fuel is burnt without enough oxygen / if incomplete combustion occurs *(1 mark)*.

   b) Carbon monoxide can interfere with the blood's role of carrying oxygen around the body, meaning it can carry less *(1 mark)*.

2 a) There is a greater demand for short-chain hydrocarbons than for longer-chain hydrocarbons *(1 mark)*. To meet this demand, long hydrocarbons are split into more useful short-chain molecules *(1 mark)*. Cracking also produces alkenes *(1 mark)* which are used to make polymers/plastic *(1 mark)*.

b) i) The paraffin is soaked into the mineral wool *(1 mark)*.

   ii) It acts as a catalyst / catalyses the reaction *(1 mark)*.

   iii) alkenes *(1 mark)*

3 a) i) high temperatures *(1 mark)*

   ii) E.g. in a car engine *(1 mark)*.

b) nitric acid *(1 mark)*

c) i) sulfur dioxide *(1 mark)*

   ii) E.g. lakes become acidic and plants and animals can die as a result / trees are killed *(1 mark for each correct answer)*.

4 E.g. most addition polymers are inert/don't react easily *(1 mark)*. This means that it takes a very long time for them to biodegrade and they can stay unchanged in landfill sites for a long time *(1 mark)*.

5 a) hydrocarbons *(1 mark)*

b) gas *(1 mark)*, lower *(1 mark)*, condense *(1 mark)*, up *(1 mark)*.

c) A — refinery gases
   B — gasoline
   C — kerosene
   D — diesel
   E — fuel oil
   F — bitumen
   (3 marks for all 6 correct, 2 marks for at least 4 correct, 1 mark for at least 2 correct)

d) bitumen *(1 mark)*

e) E.g. the longer the molecule, the higher the boiling point of the fraction *(1 mark)*.

f) Any one from: e.g. for domestic central heating / as fuel for ships *(1 mark)*.

6 a) ethene *(1 mark)*

b) i)

   $$H_2C = CH-CH_3$$ *(1 mark)*

   Don't worry if you put the CH_3 in another position — as long as it's attached to one of the carbon atoms, it's still correct.

   ii) propene *(1 mark)*

7 a)

   $$-CH_2-CHCl-$$ *(1 mark)*

   The chlorine atom can be attached to any one of the carbon atoms.

b) E.g. clothes / insulation for electrical cables *(1 mark)*

8 a) condensation polymerisation *(1 mark)*

b) water *(1 mark)*, H_2O *(1 mark)*

Pages 147-149

Warm-Up Questions

1) Nitrogen and hydrogen.

2) True

3) False (the Haber process is used to make ammonia for use in, e.g., fertilisers).

Exam Questions

1

Temperature	450 °C *(1 mark)*
Pressure	2 atmospheres/atm *(1 mark)*
Catalyst	vanadium(V) oxide/V_2O_5 *(1 mark)*

2 a) Equation: $S + O_2 \rightarrow SO_2$ *(1 mark)*
   Description: sulfur is burned in air to form sulfur dioxide gas *(1 mark)*.

b) Equation: $2SO_2 + O_2 \rightleftharpoons 2SO_3$ *(1 mark for correct reactants and products, 1 mark for correct balancing)*
   Description: the sulfur dioxide is reacted with oxygen/oxidised to form sulfur trioxide *(1 mark)*.

c) Equation: $SO_3 + H_2SO_4 \rightarrow H_2S_2O_7$ *(1 mark)*
   Description: sulfur trioxide is dissolved in sulfuric acid to form oleum *(1 mark)*.

d) Equation: $H_2S_2O_7 + H_2O \rightarrow 2H_2SO_4$
   (1 mark for correct reactants and products, 1 mark for correct balancing)
   Description: oleum is diluted with water to form concentrated sulfuric acid *(1 mark)*.

3 E.g. it's used to make fertilisers *(1 mark)*, detergents *(1 mark)* and paints *(1 mark)*.

4 a) Temperature used: 450 °C *(1 mark)*
   Pressure used: 200 atm *(1 mark)*

b) iron *(1 mark)*

c) E.g. as the ammonia gas cools it condenses and liquefies *(1 mark)*, which means it is separated from the other gases and can be easily piped off *(1 mark)*. The unused hydrogen and nitrogen are recycled/re-circulated/pumped back into the reaction chamber to be used in the reaction again *(1 mark)*.

5 a) 17% *(1 mark)*

b) i) chlorine/Cl_2 *(1 mark)*

   ii) sodium hydroxide/NaOH *(1 mark)*

   iii) sodium hydroxide/NaOH *(1 mark)*

c) chlorine/Cl_2 *(1 mark)*, sodium hydroxide/NaOH *(1 mark)*

d) chlorine/Cl_2 *(1 mark)*

6 a) $N_2 + 3H_2 \rightleftharpoons 2NH_3$
   (1 mark for correct reactants and products, 1 mark for correct balancing)

b) Reactant: nitrogen *(1 mark)* Source: the air *(1 mark)*
   Reactant: hydrogen *(1 mark)* Source: natural gas/cracking of hydrocarbons *(1 mark)*

c) E.g. nitric acid *(1 mark)* and fertiliser *(1 mark)*

7 a) sodium chloride in water *(1 mark)*

b) Chlorine/Cl_2 *(1 mark)* collected at A *(1 mark)*.
   Sodium hydroxide/NaOH *(1 mark)* collected at B *(1 mark)*.

c) i) Half-equation: $2H^+ + 2e^- \rightarrow H_2$
   (2 marks available — 1 mark for correct reactants and products, 1 mark for correct balancing)
   What happens: Two hydrogen ions accept two electrons to become one hydrogen molecule *(1 mark)*.

   ii) Half-equation: $2Cl^- \rightarrow Cl_2 + 2e^-$
   (2 marks available — 1 mark for correct reactants and products, 1 mark for correct balancing)
   What happens: Two chloride ions each lose an electron and become one chlorine molecule *(1 mark)*.

Pages 155-176

Practice Paper — 1C

1 a)

Particle	Mass	Charge
Proton	1	+1
Neutron	1	0
Electron	1/2000	−1

(2 marks for all correct, 1 mark for at least two correct)

b) C and D *(1 mark)* — isotopes have the same number of protons but a different number of neutrons, and C and D are the only pair with the same number of protons *(1 mark)*.

c) Protons — 30 *(1 mark)*
Neutrons — 35 *(1 mark)*
Electrons — 30 *(1 mark)*

d) i) A compound is a substance made of two or more different elements *(1 mark)* that are chemically bonded together *(1 mark)*.

ii) $M_r = 65 + 32 + (4 \times 16)$ *(1 mark)* = **161** *(1 mark)*
(or 2 marks for the correct answer without any working)

2 a) Nitrogen dioxide is created when the temperature is high enough for the nitrogen and oxygen in the air to react *(1 mark)*. This often happens in car engines, which there are lots of in cities *(1 mark)*.

b) i) nitric acid + calcium carbonate → calcium nitrate + carbon dioxide + water
(2 marks if all 3 products are correct, 1 mark if 2 products are correct)

Think back to acid and metal carbonate reactions — you always get a salt, carbon dioxide and water.

ii) sulfur dioxide / nitrogen oxides *(1 mark)*

iii) E.g. acid rain causes lakes to become acidic and plants and animals die as a result. / Acid rain kills trees. *(1 mark)*

3 a) i) −101 °C *(1 mark)*

ii) It is around halfway between the melting points of bromine and fluorine *(1 mark)*.

b) It is a red-brown *(1 mark)* liquid *(1 mark)*.

c) $Br_2 + 2KI \rightarrow I_2 + 2KBr$
(1 mark for correct reactants and products, 1 mark for correct balancing)

d) i)

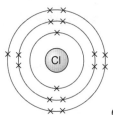

(1 mark)

ii) The group number is equal to the number of electrons in the outer electron shell *(1 mark)*.
A chlorine atom has seven electrons in its outer shell, so chlorine is in Group 7 *(1 mark)*.

e) Chlorine will displace the iodine in solution to form sodium chloride solution *(1 mark)*. This happens because chlorine is higher up Group 7 than iodine *(1 mark)*, which means that chlorine is more reactive *(1 mark)*.

f) When hydrogen chloride is dissolved in water, the hydrogen chloride molecules split up/dissociate into H^+ ions and Cl^- ions *(1 mark)*. It is the H^+ ions that make the solution acidic *(1 mark)*.

4 a) Any two from: Problem — the spots of dye/ink are touching the solvent *(1 mark)*. Correction — the student should put the filter paper in a beaker of solvent with the pencil line above the level of the solvent *(1 mark)*. / Problem — the ink and dyes are compared using different solvents *(1 mark)*. Correction — the student should use the same solvent for the black ink and the dyes so that it's a fair test *(1 mark)*. / Problem — the ink and dyes are compared on different pieces of filter paper which could make it difficult to directly compare them *(1 mark)*. Correction — the student should put the spots of the dyes and the ink on the same piece of filter paper *(1 mark)*.

b) Dyes B and D *(1 mark)*
Explanation — the spots from these two dyes are in the same positions as the spots from the black ink *(1 mark)*.

5 a) Because it has weak intermolecular forces / there are weak forces between the molecules *(1 mark)*.

Don't get confused here — the atoms within the molecules have very strong bonds, but it's the forces of attraction between the molecules that are really quite weak, giving carbon dioxide a low melting point.

b)

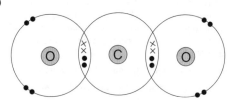

(1 mark for all shared pairs correct, 1 mark for the non-bonding electrons correct)

c) Carbon dioxide is more dense than air *(1 mark)* and so it sinks onto the flames and prevents oxygen from reaching them *(1 mark)*.

d) Division by A_r: Ca = 96.0 ÷ 40 = 2.4
C = 28.8 ÷ 12 = 2.4
O = 115.2 ÷ 16 = 7.2 *(1 mark)*
Simplest whole number ratio: 1:1:3 *(1 mark)*
Empirical formula: **$CaCO_3$** *(1 mark)*

e) i) thermal decomposition *(1 mark)*

ii) E.g. plug the reaction test tube with a bung containing a delivery tube that feeds downwards into another test tube/into a gas syringe *(1 mark)*

f) Carbon dioxide is slightly soluble in water, but becomes more soluble under pressure *(1 mark)*.

g) i) Greenhouse gases act like an insulating layer by absorbing heat that would normally be radiated from the Earth into space *(1 mark)* and re-radiating some of it back towards the Earth *(1 mark)*.

ii) 0.04% *(1 mark)*

iii) e.g. global warming / climate change / changing rainfall patterns / sea level rise *(1 mark)*

6 a)

Solution A	Solution B	Description of test	Observations	
			Solution A	Solution B
Iron(II) chloride	Iron(III) chloride	Add sodium hydroxide (NaOH) solution	Green precipitate	Reddish-brown precipitate
Sodium chloride	Sodium iodide	Add dilute nitric acid (HNO_3) followed by silver nitrate ($AgNO_3$) solution	White precipitate	Yellow precipitate

(1 mark for each test, 1 mark for each set of observations)

b) sodium carbonate / sodium hydrogen carbonate *(1 mark for identifying the sodium ion and 1 mark for identifying the carbonate ion)*

7 a) propene *(1 mark)*

b)
```
    H   H   H   H   H
    |   |   |   |   |
H — C — C — C — C — C — H
    |   |   |   |   |
    H   H   H   H   H
```
(1 mark)

c) alkenes *(1 mark)*

d) Test: Add a few drops of bromine water to the gas and shake *(1 mark)*.
Observations: Gas A (propane) will have no effect. Gas B (propene) will change the bromine water from orange to colourless *(1 mark)*.

e) The C=C double bond is split *(1 mark)* and a bromine atom is added to each carbon atom *(1 mark)*.

f) $C_3H_8 + 5O_2 \rightarrow 3CO_2 + 4H_2O$
(1 mark for products and reactants, 1 mark for balancing)

8 a) A reaction where oxygen is removed / electrons are gained *(1 mark)*.

b) i) Aluminium is more reactive than carbon (so the carbon will not be able to reduce the aluminium oxide) *(1 mark)*.

ii) It reduces the temperature needed for the process *(1 mark)*, making it cheaper *(1 mark)*.

iii) Negative electrode — $Al^{3+} + 3e^- \rightarrow Al$ *(1 mark for correct reactants and products, 1 mark for correct balancing)*
Positive electrode — $2O^{2-} \rightarrow O_2 + 4e^-$ *(1 mark for correct reactants and products, 1 mark for correct balancing)*

iv) The carbon electrode reacts with the oxygen being produced during electrolysis to produce carbon dioxide, so it is constantly being worn down *(1 mark)*.

9 a) A reaction that gives out heat energy to the surroundings *(1 mark)*.

b) E.g. measure the temperature of some water, add the substance and stir, then measure the temperature every 30 seconds and record the highest temperature reached *(1 mark)*. Repeat the experiment with other substances to determine which is the most effective *(1 mark)*. The same volume of water and mass/volume of substance should be used for each experiment *(1 mark)*.

c) $Fe_2O_3 + 3Ca \rightarrow 3CaO + 2Fe$

(1 mark for the correct reactants and products, 1 mark for correct balancing)

10 a)

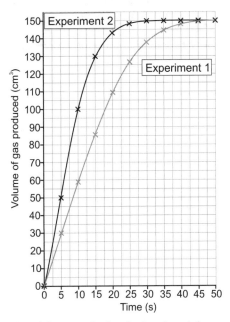

(1 mark for correctly plotted points, 1 mark for a good curve of best fit)

b) 7-8 seconds (to collect 75 cm³) *(1 mark)*

The total volume is 150 cm³, so you need to read off the value from 75 cm³ on your graph.

c) The rate of reaction decreases as the reaction proceeds *(1 mark)*.

d) It increases the rate of the reaction. The graph for experiment 2 has a steeper slope at the beginning./The reaction is complete in less time *(1 mark)*.

e) Catalysts make reactions happen faster by providing an alternative reaction pathway with a lower activation energy *(1 mark)*.

11 a) E.g. methyl orange / phenolphthalein *(1 mark)*.

b) $H_2SO_{4(aq)} + Ca(OH)_{2(aq)} \rightarrow CaSO_{4(aq)} + 2H_2O_{(l)}$

(1 mark for the correct formula for calcium sulfate, 1 mark for correctly balancing the equation)

c) i) $(8.80 \div 1000) \times 0.050 = \textbf{0.00044 moles}$ *(1 mark)*

ii) 0.00044 moles *(1 mark)*

From the equation you can see that one mole of H_2SO_4 reacts with one mole of $Ca(OH)_2$ so the number of moles of each will be the same.

iii) $0.00044 \div (10 \div 1000) = \textbf{0.044 mol/dm}^3$ *(1 mark)*

iv) $0.044 \times 74 = \textbf{3.26 g/dm}^3$ *(1 mark)*

d) i) 31.5 cm³ (accept 31 – 32 cm³) *(1 mark)*

ii) 13.5 (accept 13.4 – 13.6) *(1 mark)*

12 a) Oxygen *(1 mark)* and water *(1 mark)* must be present.

b) oxidation *(1 mark)*

c) i) sacrificial protection *(1 mark)*

ii) Magnesium is more reactive than iron *(1 mark)*, so the magnesium will be oxidised instead of the iron *(1 mark)*.

d) galvanising *(1 mark)*

13 a) Mg $MgCl_2$
    24                                  $24 + (2 \times 35.5) = 95$
    $24 \div 95 = 0.25$ g $95 \div 95 = 1$ g
    $0.25 \times 7.50 = \textbf{1.89 g}$ $1 \times 7.50 = 7.5$ g

(3 marks for correct final answer even without working, otherwise 1 mark for correctly calculating the M_rs and 1 mark for dividing through by 95 and multiplying by 7.5)

b) Test: test the gas with a lighted splint *(1 mark)*.
    Observation: hydrogen produces a squeaky pop *(1 mark)*.

14 a) i) The solid stops dissolving and remains at the bottom of the flask *(1 mark)*.

ii) zinc chloride *(1 mark)* and water *(1 mark)*

b) E.g. do a titration to find out how much acid and alkali are needed for neutralisation *(1 mark)*. Add these volumes of acid and alkali together without indicator *(1 mark)*. Heat the solution to evaporate the water, leaving a dry sample of the salt *(1 mark)*.

c) B *(1 mark)* and D *(1 mark)*

Calcium carbonate and barium sulfate are both insoluble, so they can be ruled out even though they contain the correct ions.

d) $CuCO_{3(s)} + 2HCl_{(aq)} \rightarrow CuCl_{2(aq)} + H_2O_{(l)} + CO_{2(g)}$

(1 mark for the correct products and reactants, 1 mark for balancing, 1 mark for the correct state symbols)

Pages 177-188

Practice Paper — 2C

1 a) i) Isotopes are different atomic forms of the same element, which have the same number of protons but a different number of neutrons *(1 mark)*.

ii) Cl is 25% 37Cl and 75% 35Cl *(1 mark)*
    Ar = $(37 \times 25 \div 100) + (35 \times 75 \div 100) = 35.5$ *(1 mark)*

b)

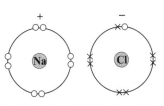

(1 mark for 8 electrons in sodium, 1 mark for 8 electrons in chlorine, 1 mark for the correct charges)

c) E.g.

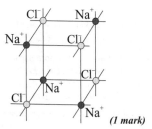

(1 mark)

d) It is held together by strong electrostatic forces of attraction between oppositely charged ions *(1 mark)*. A lot of energy is needed to overcome these forces *(1 mark)*.

It's important that you understand how the structure of a compound affects its properties.

2 a) This means that the forward and reverse reactions happen at exactly the same rate *(1 mark)*.

b) 450 °C *(1 mark)*

c) The yield of ammonia will decrease *(1 mark)*. Increasing the temperature will favour the reverse/endothermic reaction which takes in energy *(1 mark)*.

d) 200 atmospheres *(1 mark)*

e) The yield of ammonia will decrease *(1 mark)*. This is because lowering the pressure will encourage the reaction that produces more molecules (there are four molecules of gas on the left-hand side of the equation, for every two molecules on the right) *(1 mark)*.

f) iron *(1 mark)*

g) Cooling the reaction mixture liquefies the ammonia so that it can be removed *(1 mark)*. The remaining raw materials (hydrogen and nitrogen gas) can then be recycled back into the reaction *(1 mark)*.

h) E.g. making nitric acid *(1 mark)*, manufacturing fertilisers *(1 mark)*

3 a) Any two from: e.g. fizzing increases from lithium to potassium / sodium and potassium melt, but lithium doesn't / a flame is only seen with potassium *(1 mark for each correct answer)*.

b) E.g. Group 1 elements further down the group have an outer electron in a shell that is further from the nucleus *(1 mark)*. So as you go down the group, the attraction between the outer shell electron and the nucleus becomes less and so the electron is more easily lost *(1 mark)*.

c) $2Li + 2H_2O \rightarrow 2LiOH + H_2$

(1 mark for correct reactants and products, 1 mark for correct balancing)

d) The student could put the wire loop in one of the unlabelled samples and then hold it in a blue Bunsen flame *(1 mark)*.
If the flame turns crimson-red, the sample is lithium chloride, but if it turns lilac, the sample is potassium chloride *(1 mark)*.

4 a) Bonds broken $(2 \times 436) + 498 = 1370$ *(1 mark)*

Bonds formed $(4 \times 464) = 1856$ *(1 mark)*

Enthalpy change $= 1370 - 1856 = -486$ kJ/mol *(1 mark for the correct value, 1 mark for the correct sign)*

b) endothermic *(1 mark)*

5 a)

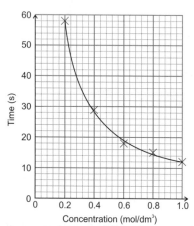

(1 mark for plotting points correctly, 1 mark for sensible line of best fit)

b) accept 22-24 s *(1 mark)*

c) Repeat the experiment and take the mean of the results *(1 mark)*.

d) The rate increases as the concentration increases *(1 mark)*.

e) At higher concentration there are more particles in a certain space / the particles are closer together *(1 mark)*. This means that collisions between particles happen more often / there are more frequent collisions / there are more collisions per second *(1 mark)*.

f) No. The magnesium has a larger surface area *(1 mark)*. This will increase the rate of the reaction *(1 mark)*, so it will take less than 18 seconds for 20 cm3 of hydrogen to form *(1 mark)*.

6 a)

H   H
| |
C = C
| |
H   H *(1 mark)*

b) Addition polymers are usually inert, which means they do not easily biodegrade *(1 mark)*.

c) poly(ethene) — e.g. packaging / plastic bags / bottles *(1 mark)*

poly(propene) — e.g. kettles / food containers / carpets *(1 mark)*

poly(chloroethene) — e.g. clothes / pipes / insulation for electrical cables *(1 mark)*

d) i)   condensation polymerisation *(1 mark)*

ii)   A small molecule, such as water *(1 mark)*.

7 a) So the ions are free to move *(1 mark)* so they can carry the current / conduct electricity *(1 mark)*.

b) $2Cl- \rightarrow Cl2 + 2e-$ *(1 mark)*

c) The sodium ions are more reactive than the hydrogen ions, so the hydrogen ions accept the electrons more easily *(1 mark)*.

d) sodium hydroxide *(1 mark)*

e) 20 minutes $\times 60 = 1200$ seconds
charge $= 4 \times 1200 = 4800$ coulombs *(1 mark)*
$4800 \div 96000 = 0.05$ faradays *(1 mark)*
2 moles of electrons produce 1 mole of H_2, so
$0.05 \div 2 = 0.025$ moles of H_2 produced *(1 mark)*,
0.025 moles of H_2 (with $M_r = 2$) has a mass of
$0.025 \times 2 = \textbf{0.05 g}$ *(1 mark)*

(4 marks awarded for correct final answer without working)

Working Out Your Grade

- Do both exam papers.
- Use the answers to mark each exam paper.
- Use the tables below to record your marks.

Paper 1

Q	Mark	Q	Mark
1		8	
2		9	
3		10	
4		11	
5		12	
6		13	
7		14	
	Total		/120

Paper 2

Q	Mark	Q	Mark
1		5	
2		6	
3		7	
4			
	Total		/60

- Add together your marks for the two papers to give a total mark out of 180.

Total Mark = Paper 1 Total + Paper 2 Total

Total Mark = ☐ / 180

- Look up your total mark in this table to see what grade you got.

Total Mark	Grade
139	A*
121	A
103	B
85	C
73	D
62	E
50	F
39	G
0	U

Important!

The grade boundaries above are given as a guide only.
Exam boards tinker with their boundaries each year, so any grade you get on these practice papers is no guarantee of getting that grade in the real exams — but it should give you a pretty good idea.

Index

Index

Index

CFSI41